GERMAN
VERBS MADE EASY
WORKBOOK

Learn German Verbs and
Conjugations The Easy Way

Lingo Mastery

ISBN: 978-1-951949-73-0

INHALTSVERZEICHNIS
CONTENTS

VORWORT
PREFACE

There is a quote by polyglot and linguist Michael Thomas that goes: "If you know how to handle the verbs, you know how to handle the language. Everything else is just vocabulary". Although there certainly are more elements involved in acquiring a foreign language, it is a quote that can serve to highlight the importance of verbs in the context of language learning. Imagine a sentence like "I a house". Surely you can appreciate how devoid of meaning this string of words is without something that turns it into an actual, meaningful sentence. And that is precisely where verbs come in. They are at the heart of every sentence; they give it meaning and bring all its other parts to life. The above sentence could thus go into many different directions, depending on the verb you intend to use: I *want* a house, I *bought* a house, I *will sell* a house, I *have built* a house...

Just like in English, verbs are an integral part of the German language. You may already have some familiarity with other aspects of German grammar, such as nouns and their different cases or the German adjective endings. However, no matter which way you approach the German language, you will find that all parts of speech are connected to and influenced by the manner in which verbs function within a sentence. With that in mind, this workbook aims to improve your German fluency by:

- Increasing the number of German verbs that you can actively use;

- Providing you with an in-depth understanding of the different forms, tenses, and moods in which German verbs can be used;

- Raising your awareness of how verbs are connected to and interact with other parts of speech.

This book takes levels A1 + A2 of the CEFR framework as an approximate guideline for its grammatical content and, as such, is directed at beginner learners of German. However, intermediate learners may also benefit from reviewing individual chapters or topics and from working on the numerous exercises that come with each chapter.

We are confident that this book will significantly broaden your vocabulary, sharpen your grammar skills, and deepen your understanding of how German verbs work in context. Moreover, we hope that it will make your language learning an intellectually stimulating and fun endeavor that will keep you coming back for more as you work your way towards German proficiency.

EINLEITUNG
INTRODUCTION

In the preface we already talked about how verbs are tremendously important for any language learner. Verbs tell us about the **actions**, **events**, or **states** of somebody or something in a sentence. They make things happen, in other words. This is also why they are sometimes referred to as *Tunwörter* ("Doing-words") or *Tätigkeitswörter* ("Action words") in German. In fact, a sentence is only considered a proper sentence if it contains a verb, since it would not carry much meaning otherwise:

You money		You **earn** money.
I day by day	do not make sense without verbs $\longrightarrow$	I **live** day by day.
Me your number		**Give** me your number.

Furthermore, verbs contain a great amount of information about what is happening in a sentence, which is reflected in the grammatical form they appear in. They tell us who is carrying out the action in a sentence (grammatical **person**), whether there are one or more people involved in the action (grammatical **number**), and when the action takes place (grammatical **tense**). Verbs also serve to emphasize whether the person performing the action (**active**) or the action itself (**passive**) is the focal point of a sentence. Lastly, they allow us to distinguish between real or hypothetical events, wishes, and commands, which can each be expressed using a different verb form.

Working through this book will equip you with the verbs you need in order to express yourself in German with a great deal of nuance. Not only will you gain an understanding of most of the relevant grammar concepts surrounding verbs, you will also broaden your comprehension of how German works as a whole. This will stand you in good stead for any further study of the language, no matter what topic you decide to focus on next.

HINWEISE ZUR BENUTZUNG DIESES BUCHES
NOTES ON HOW TO USE THIS BOOK

This book is primarily aimed at beginner learners of German. Therefore, we recommend working through the individual chapters as they appear in the book if you have no prior German knowledge at all or if you are only marginally familiar with the language. Readers with some basic or intermediary German knowledge may find it helpful to work through those chapters that deal with topics that are of particular interest to them or that cover areas where they feel they could benefit from refreshing their memory.

The book is divided into three major units:

- **Unit 1 — Basic Concepts:**
  This unit contains a number of foundational concepts and definitions, along with an overview of the relevant grammatical models surrounding German verbs.

- **Unit 2 — Tenses:**
  In this unit we will have a detailed look at all possible German verb tenses, how they are formed, and when they are used.

- **Unit 3 — Verb Voice and Verb Mood:**
  In the last unit we will learn about the most important verb phenomena besides tenses, such as the passive voice, different verb moods, the two *Konjunktiv* forms (German subjunctive), and more.

All three units are further sub-divided into chapters, each focusing on a particular grammar topic or concept. Every chapter contains a short introductory German text, set of sentences, or dialogue which highlights the grammatical subject to be discussed. Vocabulary lists with any unknown words are provided alongside each text or dialogue. Here, we made a distinction between verbs and other parts of speech since verbs are the focus of this book and should be given a more prominent look. The introductory texts and vocabulary lists are followed by a grammar section with explanations and examples. At the end of each chapter, you will find a set of exercises for you to practice what you have learned. A solution key to all the exercises is provided at the end of the book.

 This headphone symbol next to the heading of a text, dialogue or exercise indicates that audio content is available for the corresponding section.

 This headphone with a pencil next to an exercise means that you will need to refer to the corresponding audio content to complete the exercise.

Throughout the book we have included info-boxes with additional content, tips, and recommendations:

ⓘ GUT ZU WISSEN

Facts and explanations about culture and language use in Germany, Austria, and Switzerland.

☞ DENK DARAN!

Useful tips and recommendations for learning German.

VERB LISTS ...	GENERAL VOCABULARY LISTS ...	GRAMMAR OVERVIEW TABLES ...
... are presented in this shade and accompany the introductory German text or dialogue of each chapter. They may also appear alongside the grammatical explanations within a chapter, where they may contain additional verbs sorted by topic or a set of useful phrases, depending on context.	... are presented in this shade and cover any vocabulary other than verbs from the introductory texts or dialogues.	...are presented in this shade and contain concise grammatical overviews, often supplemented with example sentences and expressions.

LIST OF ABBREVIATIONS:

Acc.	———	accusative
adj.	———	adjective
adv.	———	adverb
art.	———	article
coll.	———	colloquialism
conj.	———	conjunction
Dat.	———	dative
etw.	———	etwas (something)
fml.	———	formal
idiom	———	idiomatic expression
infml.	———	informal
interj.	———	interjection
jmdm.	———	jemandem (= to someone; Dat.)
jmdn.	———	jemanden (= someone; Acc.)
lit.	———	literally
n.	———	noun
part.	———	particle
pron.	———	pronoun
v.	———	verb

HOW TO GET THE AUDIO FILES

Some of the exercises throughout this book come with accompanying audio files.
You can download these audio files if you head over to
www.lingomastery.com/german-vme-audio

ANLEITUNG ZUR AUSSPRACHE
PRONUNCIATION GUIDE

Before we begin with the first unit and its chapters, we would like to provide you with a few general guidelines to the way in which German is pronounced. German is a phonetic language and, by and large, it is pronounced as it is written. Moreover, a significant number of German sounds can be imitated quite well by using English equivalent sounds. Please remember, though, that the English examples provided in the following lists are approximations, rather than exact imitations. It is therefore essential that you develop your aural and verbal skills by listening to German native speakers and by imitating their pronunciation and intonation. To help you along with this, all the German example words from this pronunciation guide have been recorded by a native speaker and are included in our audio material.

 1. KONSONANTEN (Find audio on page 5.)
CONSONANTS

In most cases, German consonants are pronounced very similarly to their English counterparts. There are a few letters that require special attention as their pronunciation changes depending on their position in the word and/or the letters that precede or follow them. In particular, note the different possible pronunciations of the letters *c*, *d*, *g*, *r*, *s*, and *y*:

LETTER	IPA OF NAME	GERMAN EXAMPLE	APPROXIMATE ENGLISH SOUND
Bb	/beː/	Berg (mountain) /ˈbɛrk/ Ebbe (low tide) /ˈɛbə/	'b' as in "big"
Cc	/t͡seː/	1) 'ts'-sound before e, i, ö, and ä: Celsius /ˈt͡sɛlzi̯ʊs/ 2) 'k'-sound elsewhere: Café /kaˈfeː/	1) 'ts' as in "hits" 2) 'c' as in "cat"
Dd	/deː/	1) 't'-sound at the end of a word or between a vowel and a consonant: Rad (wheel) /raːt/ 2) 'd'-sound elsewhere: durstig (thirsty) /ˈdʊrstɪç/	1) 't' as in "eat" 2) 'd' as in "do"
Ff	/ɛf/	Fest (celebration) /fɛst/ für (for) /fyːɐ/	Same as in English
Gg	/geː/	1) gehen (to walk) /ˈgeːən/ 2) 'k'-sound at the end of a word: weg (away) /vɛk/ 3) when preceded by 'i' at the end of a word, the sound is similar to 'ch' in Scottish 'loch': billig (cheap) /ˈbɪlɪç/	1) 'g' as in "go" 2) 'ck' as in "tack" 3) 'ch' as in "loch"
Hh	/haː/	haben (to have) /ˈhaːbn/ heute (today) /ˈhɔytə/	Same as in English
Jj	/jɔt/; /jeː/	Ja (yes) /jaː/ jeder (everybody) /ˈjeːdər/	'y' as in "yes"
Kk	/kaː/	Kerze (candle) /ˈkɛrtsə/ Akte (file) /ˈaktə/	'c' as in "cat"

Ll	/ɛl/	*lang* (long) /laŋ/ *Liebe* (love) /ˈliːbə/	Same as in English
Mm	/ɛm/	*Mutter* (mother) /ˈmʊtɐ/ *arm* (poor) /arm/	Same as in English
Nn	/ɛn/	*Natur* (nature) /naˈtuːɐ/ *neben* (next to) /ˈneːbn/	Same as in English
Pp	/peː/	*Paket* (package) /paˈkeːt/ *Pelz* (fur) /pɛlts/	Same as in English
Qq	/kuː/	*Quark* (quark) /kvark/ *quälen* (to torment) /ˈkvɛːlən/	Like 'k' followed by 'v'
Rr	/ɛʁ/	1) *rot* (red) /roːt/ *Büro* (office) /byˈroː/ 2) *für* (for) /fyːɐ/ *Messer* (knife) /ˈmɛsɐ/	1) Generally rolled in the back of the mouth; think Scottish "loch" but make it vibrate 2) Soft, more like 'a'
Ss	/ɛs/	1) sharp 'z'-sound before or between vowels: *Sie* (formal You) /ziː/ 2) 'sh'-sound before p and t at the beginning of syllable: *spät* (late) /ʃpɛːt/ 3) regular 's'-sound elsewhere: *Obst* (fruits) /oːpst/	1) 'z' as in "zoo" 2) 'sh' as in "shut" 3) 's' as in "sit"
Tt	/teː/	*Tausend* (thousand) /ˈtauznt/ *tanzen* (dance) /ˈtantsn/	Same as in English
Vv	/faʊ̯/	*Vater* (father) /ˈfaːtɐ/ *Vogel* (bird) /ˈfoːgl/	'f' as in "father"

Ww	/veː/	*wie* (how) /viː/ *wahr* (true) /vaːɐ/	'v' as in "vice"
Xx	/ɪks/	*Xylophon* /ksyloˈfoːn/ *Xerxes* /kseːɐ̯ksəs/	Like 'k' followed by 's'
Yy	/ˈʏpsilɔn/	1) *Yeti* /ˈjeːti/ 2) *Sylt* /zʏlt/	1) 'y' as in "yellow" 2) Like German Umlaut 'ü'
Zz	/t͡sɛt/	*Zebra* /ˈtseːbra/ *zeigen* (to show) /ˈtsaign/	'ts' as in "hits"

2. VOKALE
VOWELS   (Find audio on page 5.)

Just like in English, there are five main vowels in German: **a**, **e**, **i**, **o**, and **u**. Their pronunciation, however, differs in that the German vowels produce a single, "pure" sound. Unlike in English, they do not glide into another sound towards the end, as would be the case with English "a" ("a-eeh") or "u" ("yoo").

Furthermore, German vowels each have a long and a short form. The **short** vowel sounds are "clipped," and thus pronounced shorter than their English equivalent. **Long** vowels retain the same "pure" vowel sound, only prolonged. As a rule of thumb, vowels are pronounced long when they are either **followed by the letter 'h'** (*'Bahn'*, *'Uhr'*) or by a **single consonant** (*'Lid'*, *'tragisch'*), or if the vowel is **doubled** (*'Haar'*, *'Beeren'*). Short vowels are mostly followed by two or more consonants (*'rennen'*, *'lassen'*).

When a German word beginning with a vowel follows a word ending with a consonant, the vowel is not usually joined up with the preceding consonant, as would be the case in English. "An apple" would sound something like 'anapple' in English, whereas *"ein Apfel"* would be pronounced as two separate words.

The following list gives examples for each of the long and short vowel forms, along with some pointers as to the corresponding English sound approximations.

VOWEL	IPA OF NAME	GERMAN EXAMPLE LONG	GERMAN EXAMPLE SHORT	APPROXIMATE ENGLISH SOUND
Aa	/aː/	1) *lahm* (lame) /laːm/ 2) *Rad* (wheel) /raːt/ 3) *Saat* (seed(s)) /zaːt/	4) *Affe* (ape) /ˈafə/	1-3) 'a' as in "father" 4) 'u' as in "hut"
Ee	/eː/	1) *Lehre* (teaching(s)) /ˈleːrə/ 2) *beten* (to pray) /ˈbeːtn/ 3) *Beere* (berry) /ˈbeːrə/	4) *rennen* (to run) /ˈrɛnən/	1-3) 'ay' as in "day" but with a purer English 'a' sound that doesn't glide towards English 'ee' at the end 4) 'e' as in "den"
Ii	/iː/	1) *ihre* (her) /ˈiːrə/ 2) *Titel* (title) /ˈtiːtl/ *There are no German words naturally containing a double 'i'. This is a combination that can only occur in compound words.*	3) *Bitte* (please) /ˈbɪtə/	1-2) 'ee' as in "seed" 3) 'i' as in "mitten"
Oo	/oː/	1) *Bohne* (bean) /ˈboːnə/ 2) *loben* (to praise) /ˈloːbn/ 3) *Moos* (moss) /moːs/	4) *Koffer* (suitcase) /ˈkɔfə/	1-3) 'o' as in "so" but without gliding at the end 4) 'o' as in British "hot"
Uu	/uː/	1) *Ruhm* (fame) /ruːm/ 2) *Ufer* (shore) /ˈuːfɐ/ *There are no German words naturally containing a double 'u'. This is a combination that can only occur in compound words.*	3) *Suppe* (soup) /ˈzʊpə/	1-2) 'oo' as in "pool" but with rounded lips and without gliding at the end. 3) 'oo' as in "foot"

3. UMLAUTE   (Find audio on page 5.)

Umlaute are altered sounds of the German vowel sounds for **a**, **o**, and **u** and they present themselves with two dots on top: *ä*, *ö*, *ü*. They are not part of the regular 26-letter German alphabet.

Their pronunciation can most closely be approximated by pronouncing a German 'a', 'o', or 'u' sound, then locking the position your lips assume for each of them respectively and adding a German 'i'-sound ('ee' as in "seed") on to each of these three letters.

UMLAUT	IPA OF NAME	GERMAN EXAMPLE	APPROXIMATE ENGLISH SOUND
Ää	/ɛː/	*Mädchen* (girl) /ˈmɛːtçən/ *Träne* (tear) /ˈtrɛːnə/ *säen* (to sow) /ˈzɛːən/	'ai' as in "air"
Öö	/øː/	*schön* (beautiful) /ʃøːn/ *Löwe* (lion) /ˈløːvə/ *Frisör* (hairdresser) /friˈzøːɐ/	'i' as in "girl" 'eu' as in French "bleu"
Üü	/yː/	*küssen* (to kiss) /ˈkʏsn/ *blühen* (to bloom) /ˈblyːən/ *Tür* (door) /tyːɐ/	*Does not exist in English.* 'u' as in French "tu"

4. DAS ESZETT ß   (Find audio on page 5.)
THE ESZETT ß

The German letter 'ß' (called 'Eszett', or 'sharp S') is not so much a letter that generates its own distinct sound, but more of a spelling convention that sometimes replaces a double 's'. It generally produces a 'hissing' s-sound, much like the double 's' in "boss" or "loss". You will notice that there are in fact many German words containing a double 's', instead of an Eszett, while producing the exact same sound.

LETTER	IPA OF NAME	GERMAN EXAMPLE	APPROXIMATE ENGLISH SOUND
ßß	/ɛsˈtsɛt/, /ˈʃaʁfəs ɛs/	*Straße* (street) /ˈʃtraːsə/ *groß* (tall) /ɡroːs/ *weiß* (white) /vais/	'ss' as in "boss"

 ## 5. DIPHTHONGE   (Find audio on page 5.)
DIPHTHONGS

Diphthongs are vowel combinations occurring in one syllable. They start out as one vowel and glide towards another. The most common German diphthongs are listed below and can be imitated quite well using an English sound approximation.

DIPHTHONG	IPA	GERMAN EXAMPLE	APPROXIMATE ENGLISH SOUND
ai / ei	/ai/	*beide* (both) /ˈbaidə/ *laichen* (to spawn) /ˈlaiçn̩/	'y' as in "my"
au	/au/	*Bauer* (farmer) /ˈbaʊɐ/	'ow' as in "cow"
eu / äu	/ɔy/	*heute* (today) /ˈhɔytə/ *Käufer* (buyer) /ˈkɔyfɐ/	'oy' as in "boy"
ie	/iː/	*sieben* (seven) /ˈziːbn̩/	'ee' as in "seed"

 ## 6. KONSONANTENGRUPPEN   (Find audio on page 5.)
CONSONANT GROUPS

Consonant groups are frequently occurring consonant clusters with a consistent pronunciation. Among these, special attention must be given to the pronunciation of the German *'ch'*, which can produce four different sounds. Number 2) is the sound variant that you will most frequently encounter. In addition, note that there is no English 'th'-sound in German and that the German consonant group *'th'* simply produces a /t/ sound.

CONSONANT GROUP	IPA	GERMAN EXAMPLE	APPROXIMATE ENGLISH SOUND
ch	1) /x/ After 'a', 'o', 'u' and 'au' 2) /ç/ After 'i', 'e', 'ä', 'ö', 'ü', 'ei', 'ai', 'eu', and 'äu' 3) /ks/ Before 's' 4) /k/ At the start of a word and followed by the letters 'r', 'l', 'a', or 'o'	1) *Bach* (stream) /bax/ 2) *reich* (rich) /raiç/ 3) *Dachs* (badger) /daks/ 4) *Chaos* (chaos) /ˈkaːɔs/	1) 'ch' as in Scottish "loch" 2) 'h' as in "huge" 3) 'x' as in "oxen" 4) 'k' as in "kitten"
ck	/k/	*Rock* (skirt) /rɔk/ *backen* (to bake) /ˈbakn/	hard 'k'-sound 'ck' as in "luck'
pf	/pf/	*Apfel* (apple) /ˈapfl/ *Pferd* (horse) /pfeːɐt/	'pf' as in "stepfather" but pronounced as one explosive sound.
ph	/f/	*Alphabet* (alphabet) /alfaˈbeːt/ *Philosophie* (philosophy) /filozoˈfiː/	same as in English
sch	/ʃ/	*Schule* (school) /ˈʃuːlə/ *Asche* (ashes) /ˈaʃə/	'sh' as in "cash"
th	/t/	*Theater* (theater) /teˈaːtɐ/ *Athen* (Athens) /aˈteːn/	't' as in "take" *There is no English 'th'-sound in German*

Unit 1
BASIC CONCEPTS

In this first one of three larger units, we will provide you with a number of foundational concepts and topics surrounding verbs. As such, you will be able to better contextualize other grammar points further along in this book. We also hope that Unit 1 will help to close any potential gaps you might have regarding grammar terminology. After an introductory chapter concerning different verb forms, we will outline different types of verbs, such as modal and auxiliary verbs, as well as verbs with separable and inseparable prefixes in the ensuing chapters. This will be followed by an overview of the different tenses before we wrap this unit up with a chapter on the German word order in relation to verbs.

KAPITEL 1 — VERBEN UND VERSCHIEDENE VERBFORMEN
CHAPTER 1 - VERBS AND DIFFERENT VERB FORMS

 In the introduction we already mentioned the fact that verbs convey the actions, events, or states expressed in a sentence. They do this by adopting and appearing in many different forms. Have a look at the following example sentences:

Klavier **spielen** ist mein Hobby.	Playing the piano is my hobby.
Es ist verboten, zu nahe an den Gleisen zu **stehen**.	It is not allowed to stand too close to the railroad tracks.
Mit seinem Schlüsselbund **spielend** sah er mich an.	He looked at me, playing with his key chain.
An der Ampel **stehend** wartete sie, bis es grün wurde.	Standing at the traffic light, she was waiting for it to turn green.
Im Konzert wurde ein Stück von Beethoven **gespielt**.	A piece by Beethoven was played at the concert.
Wir haben lange am Taxistand **gestanden**.	We have been standing at the taxi stand for a long time.
Du **stehst** im Garten.	You are standing in the backyard.
Er sagte, du **stehest** im Garten.	He said you were standing in the backyard.
Steh gerade!	Stand straight.
Wir **spielen** Karten.	We are playing cards.
In dieser Kneipe wird oft Darts **gespielt**.	Darts is often played in this pub.
Gestern **spielten** sie Fußball.	They played soccer yesterday.
Gestern **stand** sie lange auf dem Balkon.	She was standing on the balcony for a long time yesterday.

GERMAN VERB	ENGLISH	GERMAN VERB	ENGLISH
sein	(to) be	ansehen	(to) look at
spielen	(to) play	warten	(to) wait
haben	(to) have	stehen	(to) stand
sagen	(to) say	werden	(to) become

GENERAL VOCABULARY	ENGLISH	GENERAL VOCABULARY	ENGLISH
(das) Klavier [n.]	piano	an [prep.]	at, by
mein [pron.]	my	den [art. Dat.]	the
(das) Hobby [n.]	hobby	mit [prep.]	with
es [pron.]	it	seinem [pron. Dat.]	his
verboten [adj.]	forbidden, not allowed	(der) Schlüsselbund [n.]	key chain
zu [adv.]	too	er [pron.]	he
nahe [adj.]	close, near	mich [pron. Acc.]	me
(die) Gleise [n.]	railroad tracks	(die) Ampel [n.]	traffic light
sie [pron.]	she; they	bis [prep.]	until
es [pron.]	it	grün [adj.]	green
im [prep.]	in the	(das) Konzert [n.]	concert
ein [art.]	a	(das) Stück [n.]	(music) piece
von [prep.]	from, by	wir [pron.]	we
lange [adv.]	(for) a long time	am [prep. Dat.]	at the
(der) Taxistand [n.]	taxi stand	du [pron.]	you
(der) Garten [n.]	backyard, garden	(die) Karten [n. pl.]	cards
dieser [pron.]	this	(die) Kneipe [n.]	bar, pub
oft [adv.]	often	(das) Darts [n.]	darts
gestern [adv.]	yesterday	sie [pron.]	they; she
sie [pron.]	she	(der) Fußball [n.]	soccer
auf [prep.]	on	(der) Balkon [n.]	balcony
gerade [adv.]	straight		

All the above sentences use various forms of the verbs *spielen* (to play) and *stehen* (to stand). Do not worry if you do not yet fully understand the sentences or the individual verb forms. We will now take the above example sentences and use them to demonstrate several concepts concerning the German verb forms.

1.1 INFINITE VERBEN
NON-FINITE VERBS

Although we have so far explained that verbs can tell us about all those wonderful things such as person, tense, or number, the first verb form we are going to look at does not show us any of these characteristics (at least not on their own). The verb form we are talking about here is called **non-finite verbs** and the good thing about them is that they remain unchanged, since they are not conjugated. However, this also means that they cannot indicate a grammatical number or person on their own.

In German (as in English), there are three different non-finite verb forms: the *Infinitiv* (infinitive), the *Partizip Präsens* (present participle), and the *Partizip Perfekt* (past participle).

1.1.1 Infinitive

The **infinitive** is the basic form of the verb as you would find it in a dictionary. In English, this form is often listed together with the particle "to", as in '(to) eat' or '(to) live'. In German, the vast majority of verbs form the infinitive by adding the endings *'-en'*, *'-ern'*, or *'eln'* to the **stem** of the verb:

infinitive	stem		
spielen	*spiel-*	*en*	
warten	*wart-*	*en*	⟶ **infinitive endings**
stehen	*steh-*	*en*	

1.1.2 Present Participle

The **present participle** ('Partizip Präsens' or 'Partizip I' in German) is sometimes also referred to as *'Mittelwort der Gegenwart'* (middle word of the present) because it is not quite a verb and not quite an adjective, as it were. One striking feature of the present participle is its usage in describing ongoing activities. In English, the present participle is easily recognized by its '-ing' ending ('playing', 'standing') and often used as the main verb in compound tenses ('I am playing') or as an adjective ('Peter is a loving son').

Mit seinem Schlüsselbund spielend sah er mich an.

An der Ampel stehend wartete sie, bis es grün wurde.

Although these two examples use the present participle in an adverbial way (they describe the way in which the main verbs 'ansehen' and 'warten' are carried out), it is more common to see it used as an adjective in German. In that case, the present participle will also take the adjective endings, as grammatically required for each scenario:

*Peter ist ein lieben**der** Sohn.*

However, getting into the different grammar rules for adjective endings is beyond the scope of this chapter. For now, the most important thing is for you to recognize a present participle when you see one.

1.1.3 Past Participle

The **past participle** is called 'Partizip Perfekt' or 'Partizip II' in German. Analogously to the Partizip Präsens, it is also referred to as *'Mittelwort der Vergangenheit'* (middle word of the past). In English, it can be recognized by its ending **-ed**, as in 'play**ed**' or 'liv**ed**'. There are irregular past participle forms as well, such as 'spok**en**' or 'do**ne**'. In conjunction with a conjugated form of the auxiliary verbs '(to) be' or '(to) have' (of which more in Chapter 3), the past participle serves to form the passive or the present perfect, respectively:

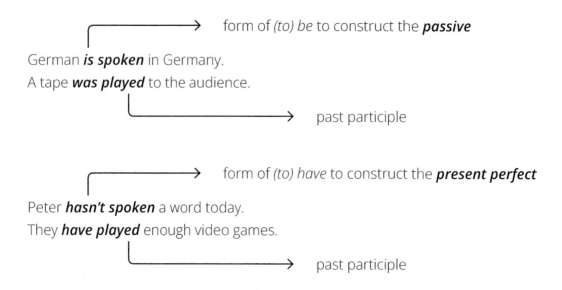

form of *(to) be* to construct the ***passive***

German ***is spoken*** in Germany.
A tape ***was played*** to the audience.

past participle

form of *(to) have* to construct the ***present perfect***

Peter ***hasn't spoken*** a word today.
They ***have played*** enough video games.

past participle

The German past participle takes different forms, depending on whether a verb is **regular** or **irregular** (→ cf. 1.5). While most regular verbs form their past participle in a predictable way, the past participles of irregular verbs must be memorized. Just like in English, the German past participle is used to form the **perfect tense** and the **passive**, together with one of the auxiliary verbs **haben**, **sein** (perfect) or **werden** (passive).

To form the past participle, German **regular verbs** add the prefix **ge-** and the ending **-t** to the stem of the infinitive verb:

German **irregular verbs** often undergo a change to their stem vowel, and occasionally to some of their consonants, when forming the past participle. The prefix **ge-** and the ending **-en** or **-n** are usually added to the stem:

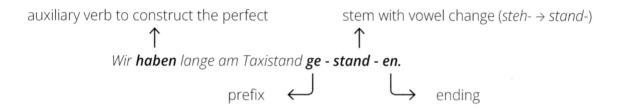

There are several other aspects concerning the formation and usage of the past participle. Chapter 8 in Unit 2 of this book will discuss those in more detail.

1.2 VERBSTAMM UND VERBENDUNG
VERB STEM AND VERB ENDING

In the previous section we already learned that every German verb has a **stem** that can be identified by taking away the verb's infinitive ending:

sagen: **sag** ——— en
stehen: **steh** ——— en
         ↑
       stem

Once we identify the verb stem, we can add many different endings to the verb, which is where the concept of **conjugation** comes in. Conjugated verbs are verbs which have been changed to communicate person, number, tense, voice, and mood. While the previous section dealt with non-finite verbs which do not clearly show any of these parameters on their own, a conjugated verb is considered a **finite** verb form that possesses some or all of these characteristics.

These finite verb forms can, for example, come in the shape of the different tenses, each featuring three grammatical persons for the singular and three grammatical persons for the plural:

*Du **stehst** im Garten.* ⟶ The ending '-st' added on to the stem 'steh- ', indicates 2nd person singular in the present tense. This corresponds with the 2nd person pronoun *"du"*.

In Unit 2 we will have a much more detailed look at the different tenses and their conjugations. For now, it is important to be familiar with the concept of a conjugated (finite) verb, as opposed to the non-finite verbs described above.

1.3 INDIKATIV, KONJUNKTIV UND IMPERATIV
INDICATIVE, SUBJUNCTIVE, AND IMPERATIVE

Another characteristic that finite verbs can express is called the **mood** of the verb. The mood that a verb possesses marks the activity in a sentence as either factual (**indicative**), hypothetical (**subjunctive**) or as an order given to somebody else (**imperative**).

The **indicative** is a type of mood that is used for making statements or asking questions of a factual kind. It can occur in all German tenses.

*Du **stehst** im Garten.* ⟶ Factual statement: 2nd person, singular, indicative, present

There are two types of **subjunctive** moods in German, called *Konjunktiv I* and *Konjunktiv II*. The subjunctive moods can each occur in four different tenses.

While the Konjunktiv II is used to express hypothetical events or wishes, the Konjunktiv I is primarily used to form sentences in indirect speech:

Konjunktiv I: *Er sagte, du **stehest** im Garten.*
                 He said you were standing in the backyard.

Konjunktiv II: *Ich wünschte, du **stündest** im Garten.*
                 I wish you were standing in the backyard.

The **imperative** is a mood we can use to express orders given to one or more people. This is also why it only occurs in the 2nd person singular and plural:

Steh *gerade!* $\longrightarrow$ Order addressing one person (singular)

Steht *gerade!* Order addressing several people (plural)

A more detailed description of all these different verb moods will be given in Unit 3. In the meantime, just remember the three moods a verb can appear in and keep in mind what purpose they each serve.

1.4 AKTIV UND PASSIV
ACTIVE AND PASSIVE

Most actions can be looked at from two different angles:

Widerrechtlich abgestellte Fahrzeuge werden kostenpflichtig abgeschleppt!

1) *Die Gäste spielen in dieser Kneipe oft Darts.*
   (The patrons often play darts in this pub.)

2) *In dieser Kneipe wird oft Darts gespielt.*
   (Darts is often played in this pub.)

Both sentences inform us that playing darts is a popular activity in a certain pub. However, in the first sentence the emphasis is on the *Gäste* (guests, patrons) who often play darts there, while in the second sentence the important piece of information is the frequent playing of darts taking place in that pub. We call this distinction the **voice** of a verb. The voice of a verb can either be **active** (sentence 1) or **passive** (sentence 2).

In an **active** sentence, the attention is usually on an agent carrying out the action (*'die Gäste'*), while the object of the sentence receives the action (in this case the game of darts as it is being played by the guests). Active sentences are far more common than passive sentences in German, and, in most instances, they are considered stylistically preferrable.

In a **passive** sentence, the focus is shifted to what was previously the object (the game of darts) and to the fact that it is being played. Here, it is not important (or perhaps even unknown) who is doing the playing. The German passive voice is formed by using the relevant tense of the auxiliary verb **werden** + the **past participle** (→ cf. 1.1.3):

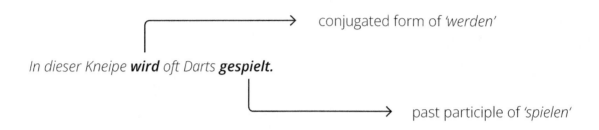

conjugated form of 'werden'

*In dieser Kneipe **wird** oft Darts **gespielt.***

past participle of 'spielen'

1.5 REGELMÄSSIGE UND UREGELMÄSSIGE VERBEN
REGULAR AND IRREGULAR VERBS

Most European languages distinguish between **regular** and **irregular** verbs. In German, regular verbs are also referred to as *"schwache Verben"* (weak verbs), while irregular verbs are often called *"starke Verben"* (strong verbs). This distinction becomes visible when looking at the simple past and past participle forms. In English, for example, the verb **(to) play** forms the simple past and past participle according to a predictable pattern, namely by adding '-ed': **play - played - played**. The verb **(to) go**, on the other hand, has irregular forms for both the simple past and the past participle: **go - went - gone**.

Fortunately, most German verbs are regular and there are only about 200 irregular verbs. The most important thing to remember about German irregular verbs is the fact that they undergo a **vowel change** in the simple past and past participle (sometimes also in 2nd and 3rd person of the present tense):

	SPIELEN REGULAR	STEHEN IRREGULAR
INFINITIVE	spiel - en	steh - en
SIMPLE PAST	spiel - te	st**a**nd
PAST PARTICIPLE	ge - spiel - t	ge - st**a**nd - en

Further aspects of German irregular verbs will be explained in the different chapters about tenses of Unit 2. We also provide a list of German irregular verbs in the appendix of this book.

ÜBUNGEN
EXERCISES

 **Ü 1.1)** In the following e-mail, the dots for the German *Umlaute* have been left out. Listen to the audio recording very carefully and decide which of the vowels should be *Umlaute*.

Hallo Karin,

Ich hoffe, dir geht es gut. Ich freue mich schon auf nachste Woche! Es ist schon so lange her, dass wir uns gesehen haben. Falls moglich, nehme ich am Montag den fruhen Zug, damit ich nicht so spat ankomme. Konntest du mich bitte vom Bahnhof abholen? Das Taxi ist immer so unverschamt teuer. Ich bringe auch Weihnachtsgeback mit! Also dann, bis bald und liebe Gruße!

Anna

Ü 1.2) Have a look at the following German non-finite verb forms. Decide which of them are in the infinitive, the present participle, or the past participle and put them in the correct column.

fahren, erklärend, geklettert, sehen, gesungen, erzählend, geraucht, erkennen, geleert, ablenkend, gejuckt, gegossen, lesen, verteilend, abnehmen, gerannt, verstehend, lenken

INFINITIVE	PRESENT PARTICIPLE	PAST PARTICIPLE

Ü 1.3) What is meant by *"Indikativ"*, *"Konjunktiv I"*, *"Konjunktiv II"*, and *"Imperativ"*? What purpose does each of them serve?

_____

_____

_____

Ü 1.4) Decide if the sentences below are each in the active or the passive voice. In active sentences, underline the verb. In passive sentences, underline the conjugated form of *"werden"* and the past participle of the verb.

a) Das Buch wird gelesen.

Voice: _____

b) Der Mann wartete seit Stunden auf den Zug.

Voice: _____

c) Wir haben einen großen Balkon.

Voice: _____

d) Das alte Klavier wurde über die Jahre hinweg viel gespielt.

Voice: _____

e) In der Schweiz werden hauptsächlich drei Sprachen gesprochen.

Voice: _____

f) Die gesprochenen Sprachen sind Deutsch, Französisch und Italienisch.

Voice: _____

KAPITEL 2 — MODALVERBEN
CHAPTER 2 - MODAL VERBS

 Most verbs are capable of completing a sentence on their own. We call such verbs **main verbs** (*"Vollverben"*). However, there is a group of verbs that cannot usually complete a sentence on their own. Those verbs require a companion in the shape of a main verb to get their meaning across. Such verbs are called **modal verbs** (*"Modalverben"*). Have a look at the following examples:

Ich **kann** *das nicht verstehen.*	I cannot understand that.
Wir **müssen** *um sieben Uhr zuhause sein.*	We have to be at home at seven o'clock.
Darf *er auch zur Party kommen?*	May he come to the party, too?
Wann **sollen** *wir anrufen?*	When should we call?
Wollt *ihr meine neue Wohnung sehen?*	Do you want to see my new apartment?
Ich **möchte** *eine Fahrkarte kaufen.*	I would like to buy a ticket.

GERMAN VERB	ENGLISH	GERMAN VERB	ENGLISH
können	(to) be able to, can	kommen	(to) come
verstehen	(to) understand	sollen	(to) be supposed to, should
müssen	(to) have to, must	anrufen	(to) call
dürfen	(to) be allowed to, may	wollen	(to) want to
sehen	(to) see	kaufen	(to) buy
mögen	(to) like to		

GENERAL VOCABULARY	ENGLISH	GENERAL VOCABULARY	ENGLISH
ich [*pron.*]	I	zuhause [*adv.*]	(at) home
das [*pron.*]	that	auch [*adv.*]	also, too
nicht [*adv.*]	not	zur [*prep. Dat.*]	to the
um [*prep.*]	at (in time indications)	(die) Party [*n.*]	party
sieben [*adj.*]	seven	wann [*adv.*]	when
(die) Uhr [*n.*]	watch, clock; o'clock	ihr [*pron.*]	you (pl.)
meine [*pron.*]	my	(die) Wohnung [*n.*]	apartment, flat
eine [*art.*]	a	(die) Fahrkarte [*n.*]	ticket

2.1 ÜBERBLICK ÜBER DIE MODALVERBEN
MODAL VERBS OVERVIEW

Both English and German make use of **modal verbs**. In English, they are **"can"**, **"may"**, **"must"**, **"shall"**, **"should"**, and **"will"**. Modal verbs change or modify other verbs in a sentence to emphasize, for example, permission, ability, or necessity to do something. They cannot appear on their own and require a main verb (usually in the infinitive form) which they are modifying:

	MODAL VERB	**MAIN VERB**	
When you have time, you	**should**	visit	me.
I	**must**	find out	what she did.
We	**will**	apply	for citizenship.

Just like in English, **German modal verbs** express an attitude toward, or relationship to, an action and they modify the main verb accordingly. There are six modal verbs in German:

dürfen	may / to be allowed to
können	can / to be able to
müssen	must / to have to
sollen	to be supposed to, should, ought to
wollen	to want
mögen	to like

All the example sentences of this chapter feature modal verbs. Note how they refer to and change the meaning of what is being expressed in the main verb:

Ich möchte eine Fahrkarte kaufen.	⟶	*möchte … kaufen:*	**desire** to buy
Darf er auch zur Party kommen?	⟶	*darf … kommen:*	**permission** to come
Ich kann das nicht verstehen.	⟶	*kann … verstehen:*	**ability** to understand
Wann sollen wir anrufen?	⟶	*sollen … anrufen:*	**aptness** to call
Wollt ihr meine neue Wohnung sehen?	⟶	*wollt … sehen:*	**desire** to see
Wir müssen um sieben Uhr zuhause sein.	⟶	*müssen … sein:*	**necessity** to be

The conjugation of the German modal verbs is irregular in the present tense singular. They have no special ending in the first and third person. The plural forms, however, are regular. Additionally, five modal verbs have a vowel change:

	DÜRFEN	KÖNNEN	MÜSSEN
ich	darf	kann	muss
du	darfst	kannst	musst
er/sie/es	darf	kann	muss
wir	dürfen	können	müssen
ihr	dürft	könnt	müsst
sie/Sie	dürfen	können	müssen

	SOLLEN	WOLLEN	MÖGEN
ich	soll	will	mag
du	sollst	willst	magst
er/sie/es	soll	will	mag
wir	sollen	wollen	mögen
ihr	sollt	wollt	mögt
sie/Sie	sollen	wollen	mögen

2.2 MODALVERBEN IM DETAIL
MODAL VERBS IN DETAIL

Having outlined the conjugations for each of the modal verbs in the present tense, let us now have a look at each modal in a little more detail:

dürfen

- Expresses **permission**.

- Meaning 'to be allowed to' or 'may':

  Du darfst hier rauchen.   You are allowed to smoke here.

- Meaning 'must not' or 'may not':

  Wir dürfen hier nicht fotografieren.   We must not take pictures here.

- Expressing politeness:

  Darf ich?   May I?

können

- Expresses **ability**.

- Meaning 'can' or 'to be able to':

Kannst du mir helfen?	Can you help me?
Er kann sehr gut Tango tanzen.	He can dance Tango very well.

müssen

- Expresses **obligation** and/or **necessity**.

- Meaning 'to have to' or 'must' or 'need to':

Wir müssen nach Hause gehen.	We have to go home.
Ich muss heute arbeiten.	I must/have to work today.

- Certain common, informal uses:

Muss das sein?	Is that really necessary?
Ich muss mal auf die Toilette.	I need to use the bathroom.

- When used with the negative **nicht**, *müssen* does not convey the meaning of prohibition as in English, but means 'don't have to' or 'needn't':

Du musst morgen nicht kommen.	You needn't come tomorrow.

sollen

- Expresses **duty** or **aptness**.

- Meaning 'ought to' or 'should':

Du sollst mehr Sport treiben.	You should play more sports.
Er soll zum Arzt gehen.	He should see a doctor (lit: go to the doctor's)

- Meaning 'to be supposed to':

Was soll das bedeuten?	What is that supposed to mean?

- Meaning 'to be said to be':

Er soll sehr großzügig sein.	He is said to be very generous.

wollen

- Expresses **intention** or **desire**.

- Meaning 'to want to':

Wir wollen heute ins Kino gehen.	We want to go to the movies today.

- Meaning 'to want' or 'to wish' as an informal alternative to *mögen*:

Willst du etwas essen?	Would you like to eat something?

Note that **wollen** cannot be used in the same way that 'will' is used in English to form the future tense. The future tense in German requires the verb *'werden'*, which we will cover at a later point.

mögen

- Expresses **fondness** or **desire**.

- Meaning 'to like':

Ich mag Fussball.	I like football.
Wir mögen den Deutschlehrer.	We like the German teacher.

- Often used in the subjunctive form **'möchten'**, meaning 'would like to':

Ich möchte Briefmarken kaufen.	I would like to buy stamps.
Er möchte nach Hause gehen.	He would like to go home.

Its verb endings are regular, except for *er/sie/es*, where there is no final **-t**, and there is no stem vowel change:

ich	**möchte**	wir	**möchten**
du	**möchtest**	ihr	**möchtet**
er/sie/es	**möchte**	sie/Sie	**möchten**

In Unit 2 and 3 we are going to learn more about the way modal verbs behave in tenses other than the present and in the different verb moods.

ÜBUNGEN
EXERCISES

Ü 2.1) All of the following people cannot work because they have fallen ill. Using the modal verb *'können'*, change each of the statements to a sentence expressing that they cannot work. One example has been done for you.

Example: Ich arbeite nicht.   ⟶   Ich *kann* nicht arbeiten.

a) Peter arbeitet nicht.

_____

b) Sandra arbeitet nicht.

_____

c) Wir arbeiten nicht.

_____

d) Du arbeitest nicht.

_____

e) Herr Müller arbeitet nicht.

_____

f) Ihr arbeitet nicht.

_____

Ü 2.2) Fill in the gaps using the German equivalents of the English cues. Make sure to use the right ending as required by the grammatical person.

a) Wir_____heute Nachmittag Fußball spielen. (want)

b) Du_____hier nicht so laut reden. (not be allowed to)

c) Ich_____zuhause immer Hausschuhe tragen. (have to)

d) Mein kleiner Bruder _____ nicht Fahrrad fahren. (be able to)

e) Wir_____uns im Urlaub ausruhen. (should)

f) _____du morgen zu mir kommen? (like to)

Ü 2.3) Change the following sentences using the German modal verb provided. One example has been done for you.

Example: Wann hilfst du mir? (sollen) ⟶ *Wann sollst du mir helfen?*

a) Peter spielt Klavier. (können)

_____

b) Sandra und Erika gehen nach Hause. (müssen)

_____

c) Wir besuchen heute ein Konzert. (dürfen)

_____

d) Ich kaufe ein Auto. (wollen)

_____

e) Hans und Frank hören Musik. (mögen)

_____

Ü 2.4) The following German sentences all use modal verbs. Based on your knowledge of how each modal verb changes the meaning of the main verb, match the sentences with the intended change on the right.

(   ) a) Mein Bruder will immer fernsehen.   1) permission

(   ) b) Am Montag darf ich immer mit meiner Mutter einkaufen gehen.   2) aptness

(   ) c) Dieses Jahr möchte ich nach Griechenland in den Urlaub fahren.   3) ability

(   ) d) Ich kann meine Wohnung nicht mehr bezahlen.   4) necessity

(   ) e) Peter soll am Freitag um sieben Uhr bei mir sein.   5) desire

(   ) f) Wir müssen noch Weihnachtsgeschenke für die Kinder kaufen.   6) desire

KAPITEL 3 — HILFSVERBEN
CHAPTER 3 - AUXILIARY VERBS

Auxiliary verbs are verbs that help the main verb of a sentence form a certain tense or, in some instances, the passive voice. For this reason, they are also referred to as "helping verbs" or *"Hilfsverben"* in German. Auxiliary verbs are similar in function and behavior to modal verbs. However, while modal verbs tend to alter the mood of the main verb or emphasize a different meaning, auxiliary verbs are primarily used to indicate tenses and the passive.

 A verb tense that is formed using an auxiliary verb + a main verb is called a **compound tense**. Only the auxiliary verb is conjugated in such a construction. In the following example sentences we have highlighted both the auxiliary verb and the (non-finite form of) the main verb:

Hast du das Buch gelesen?	Have you read the book?
Ich habe deine Nachricht gestern nicht bekommen.	I did not receive your message yesterday.
Peter ist nach Hause gegangen.	Peter has gone home.
Wir sind gestern mit dem Auto nach Berlin gefahren.	We went to Berlin by car yesterday.
Ich habe das Buch noch nicht gelesen, aber ich werde es nächste Woche lesen.	I have not read the book yet, but I will read it next week.
Das Buch wird gelesen.	The book is being read.

GERMAN VERB	ENGLISH	GERMAN VERB	ENGLISH
lesen	(to) read	fahren	(to) drive, (to) go
bekommen	(to) receive, (to) get	gehen	(to) walk, (to) go

GENERAL VOCABULARY	ENGLISH	GENERAL VOCABULARY	ENGLISH
(das) Buch [*n.*]	book	deine [*pron.*]	your
(die) Nachricht [*n.*]	message	nach Hause [*adv.*]	home
(das) Auto [*n.*]	car	nach [*prep.*]	to; after
noch nicht [*adv.*]	not yet	aber [*conj.*]	but, however
nächste /-r /-es [*adj.*]	next	(die) Woche [*n.*]	week

In English, there are three auxiliary verbs whose function is similar to that of the German auxiliary verbs: '(to) **have**', '(to) **be**', and '(to) **do**'. These verbs are often used together with a main verb in the formation of tenses, in questions, or to indicate the passive voice:

	AUXILIARY VERB	+	MAIN VERB	→	EXPRESSES
Peter	**is** (Finite form of 'to be')		**driving** (Present participle of 'to drive')	a car.	Present progressive tense
I	**have** (Finite form of 'to have')		**bought** (Past participle of 'to buy')	a house.	Present perfect tense
	Does (Finite form of 'to do')	she	**know** (Verb in the infinitive)	many people?	Question
The man	**was** (Finite form of 'to be')		**arrested** (Past participle of 'to arrest')	immediately.	Passive voice

In German, there are three main auxiliary verbs: **haben** (to have), **sein** (to be), and **werden** (to become). Just like in English, they help in the construction of tenses and of the passive voice, in conjunction with a main verb. However, despite some overlap in usage, be careful not to assume that a literal translation of the English equivalent words is always possible. Let us have a look at each of the German auxiliary verbs in some more detail.

3.1 *HABEN* AND *SEIN*

The verbs *haben* and *sein* are two extremely common German verbs whose usage extends beyond their literal meaning. Even if they are used as an auxiliary verb to form a different tense with the main verb, you will most frequently conjugate them in the present tense. For this reason, let us first have a look at each of their present tense conjugations:

	SEIN			HABEN		
1st person (sing.)	*ich*	**bin**	(I am)	*ich*	**habe**	(I have)
2nd person (sing.)	*du*	**bist**	(you are)	*du*	**hast**	(you have)
3rd person (sing.)	*er/sie/es*	**ist**	(he/she/it is)	*er/sie/es*	**hat**	(he/she/it has)
1st person (pl.)	*wir*	**sind**	(we are)	*wir*	**haben**	(we have)
2nd person (pl.)	*ihr*	**seid**	(you are)	*ihr*	**habt**	(you have)
3rd person (pl.)	*sie*	**sind**	(they are)	*sie*	**haben**	(they have)
2nd person formal (sing. & pl.)	*Sie*	**sind**	(you are, *formal*)	*Sie*	**haben**	(you have, *formal*)

As you can see, both *sein* and *haben* have irregular present forms which need to be memorized.

3.1.1 Die Verwendung von *haben*
The usage of *haben*

Before we discuss the verb *haben* and its role as an auxiliary verb, we are going to briefly look at its usage and meaning when used as a main verb:

- To indicate **possession**:

  *Ich **habe** ein Haus.* (I have/own a house.)
  *Sie **hat** viel Geld.* (She has a lot of money.)

- To describe a **state of affairs**:
  (esp. in relation to a noun or person)

  *Er **hat** Zeit.* (He has time.)
  *Wir **haben** viele Freunde.*
  (We have many friends.)

- In certain **fixed expressions**:

  *Wir **haben** es eilig.* (We are in a hurry.)
  *Ich **habe** dich lieb.* (I am fond of you.)
  *Dafür ist er nicht zu **haben**.* (He is not up for that.)

When used as an **auxiliary verb**, however, *haben* serves to form a number of compound tenses, particularly the **Perfekt**, *Plusquamperfekt* and *Futur II*. While we will have a closer look at the *Plusquamperfekt* and *Futur II* tenses in Unit II, we will focus on the *Perfekt* tense for now as it is by far the most commonly used compound tense.

The German *Perfekt* tense is normally used in conversation to describe events in the past. Although it can be translated into English using either the present perfect or the simple past, the simple past is often more appropriate.

The *Perfekt* tense is formed with a finite form of *haben* (conjugated in the present tense) + the **past participle** of the main verb:

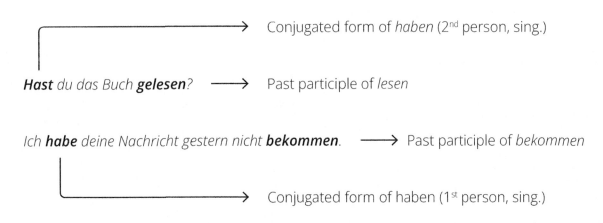

Conjugated form of *haben* (2nd person, sing.)

***Hast** du das Buch **gelesen**?* ⟶ Past participle of *lesen*

*Ich **habe** deine Nachricht gestern nicht **bekommen**.* ⟶ Past participle of *bekommen*

Conjugated form of haben (1st person, sing.)

3.1.2 Die Verwendung von *sein*
The usage of *sein*

Apart from its obvious, main-verb usage where the meaning is "to be", **sein** is also used as an auxiliary verb in compound tenses. While *haben* is the most common auxiliary verb you will need in order to form the **Perfekt** tense (as well as the *Plusquamperfekt* and *Futur II*) in German, there is a smaller group of verbs requiring *sein* to be used instead. Verbs of this category often express **movement** or a **change in condition**.

The formation of the *Perfekt* tense using *sein* follows the same pattern as with *haben*, i.e. it requires a finite form of **sein** (conjugated in the present tense) + the **past participle** of the main verb.

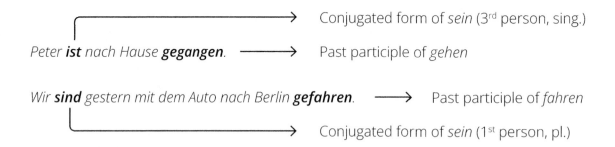

As mentioned above, the *Perfekt* tense is usually formed using the auxiliary verb *sein* if the main verb expresses **movement**, a **change in location**, or a **change in condition**. Accordingly, the above example sentences, featuring *gehen* and *fahren* as their main verbs, require *sein* for the *Perfekt* tense. The following list provides you with the most common German verbs that form the *Perfekt* tense in this way.

GERMAN VERB	ENGLISH	PERFEKT TENSE (SEIN + PAST PARTICIPLE)		
fahren	(to) drive, (to) go	ich	bin	gefahren
fallen	(to) fall	du	bist	gefallen
fliegen	(to) fly	er/sie/es	ist	geflogen
fliehen	(to) flee			geflohen
fließen	(to) flow	wir	sind	geflossen
folgen	(to) follow	ihr	seid	gefolgt
gehen	(to) walk, (to) go	sie	sind	gegangen

hüpfen	(to) leap		*gehüpft*
kommen	(to) come		*gekommen*
landen	(to) land		*gelandet*
laufen	(to) run		*gelaufen*
reisen	(to) travel		*gereist*
reiten	(to) ride		*geritten*
rennen	(to) run, (to) race	***ich* — *bin***	*gerannt*
rudern	(to) row	***du* — *bist***	*gerudert*
schwimmen	(to) swim	***er/sie/es* — *ist***	*geschwommen*
segeln	(to) sail	***wir* — *sind***	*gesegelt*
sinken	(to) sink	***ihr* — *seid***	*gesunken*
springen	(to) jump	***sie* — *sind***	*gesprungen*
steigen	(to) climb		*gestiegen*
starten	(to) start, (to) launch		*gestartet*
sterben	(to) die		*gestorben*
stürzen	(to) fall, (to) tumble		*gestürzt*
wandern	(to) hike		*gewandert*

Lastly, note that *sein*, used as an auxiliary verb, is sometimes employed to form the passive voice in certain tenses as well. In Unit 3 we will discuss this topic in more detail (→ cf. Unit 3, Ch. 13).

3.2 WERDEN

The German verb **werden** is another versatile word. As a main verb it literally means '(to) become' in sentences such as *'Die Tage werden kürzer'* (The days are getting/becoming shorter) or *'Er will Arzt werden'* (He wants to become a doctor). Apart from its usage as a main verb, however, *werden* also serves as an **auxiliary verb** to form the *Futur I* tense, as well as the **passive voice**.

3.2.1 Werden zur Bildung des Futur I
Using *werden* to form the *Futur I*

The German **future tense** is formed in a similar fashion to how you would form the English future using 'will / shall' + main verb (e.g., 'I will do my best to help you'). To form the **Futur I** tense in German, we need to be familiar with the conjugation of *werden* in the present tense:

	WERDEN	
1st person (sing.)	*ich*	**werde**
2nd person (sing.)	*du*	**wirst**
3rd person (sing.)	*er/sie/es*	**wird**
1st person (pl.)	*wir*	**werden**
2nd person (pl.)	*ihr*	**werdet**
3rd person (pl.)	*sie*	**werden**
2nd person formal (sing. & pl.)	*Sie*	**werden**

All that we then need to add to the conjugated (finite) form of *werden* is the **infinitive** of the main verb. Take a look at the following example sentence from the beginning of this chapter:

Finite form of *werden*

*Ich habe das Buch noch nicht gelesen, aber ich **werde** es nächste Woche **lesen**.*

Main verb in the infinitive

3.2.2 *Werden* zur Bildung des Passivs
Using *werden* to form the passive voice

The other instance in which *werden* serves as an auxiliary verb is the German **passive voice**. Chapter 13 of Unit 3 will address this topic in more detail since there are a number of aspects to consider when constructing the passive voice in German. For now, however, it is important to remember that a construction with *werden* is a common way to build a passive sentence. To this end, the auxiliary verb **werden** is conjugated in the relevant tense and complemented by the **past participle** of the main verb:

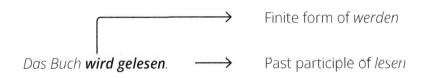

Finite form of *werden*

*Das Buch **wird gelesen**.* ⟶ Past participle of *lesen*

ÜBUNGEN
EXERCISES

Ü 3.1) The German verbs *haben*, *sein*, and *werden* can be used both as main verbs and as auxiliary verbs. In the following sentences, decide whether each of these three verbs serves as a main verb (MV) or an auxiliary verb (AV).

a) Meine Wohnung ist in München.   _____

b) Ich habe einen Brief bekommen.   _____

c) Hoffentlich wird das Wetter schön.   _____

d) Mein Vater ist letztes Jahr gestorben.   _____

e) Wir haben zwei Katzen und einen Hund.   _____

f) Das Auto wird gestartet.   _____

g) Ich bin gestern nach Hause gekommen.   _____

h) Wirst du mich nächste Woche besuchen?   _____

Ü 3.2) The following sentences are all written in the *Perfekt* tense. Decide whether *sein* or *haben* is needed to fill in each gap. Make sure to insert the correctly conjugated form of either auxiliary verb.

a) Ich_____gestern zwei Kilometer gelaufen.

b) Er_____das Buch nicht gelesen.

c) Wir_____letzte Woche den neuen James-Bond-Film gesehen.

d) _____ihr mit dem Bus gefahren?

e) Das Flugzeug_____gelandet.

f) Sie_____dich nicht verstanden.

Ü 3.3) Turn the following active sentences into passive ones by using the auxiliary verb _werden_. One example has been done for you.

Example:

Er liest das Buch. $\longrightarrow$ Das Buch wird gelesen.

a) Ich starte das Auto. _____

b) Sie fährt den Bus. _____

c) Wir sehen die Männer. _____

d) Er kauft das Haus. _____

KAPITEL 4 — VERBEN MIT TRENNBAREM UND UNTRENNBAREM PRÄFIX
CHAPTER 4 - VERBS WITH SEPARABLE AND INSEPARABLE PREFIXES

Many German verbs begin with **prefixes**, such as *zu-*, *mit-*, *aus-*, or *ein-*, that change or add to the meaning of the base verb they are attached to. In a sense, this is similar to the concept of English phrasal verbs, whereby certain prepositions can change the meaning of the main verb when used together as a fixed expression. For example, phrasal verbs such as '(to) make up' or '(to) take off' have quite a different meaning from that of their original base verbs '(to) make' and '(to) take'.

 German verbs with prefixes are always written as one word in the infinitive. It is important to note, however, that some of them are separated from the verb once the verb is conjugated. Have a look at the following short dialogue between Klaus and Tina at the supermarket:

Klaus: Hallo Tina! Na, musst du auch **einkaufen** gehen?	Klaus: Hi Tina! So, you have to go shopping, too?
Tina: Ja, ich muss meinen Kindern Schokolade **mitbringen**. Was **kaufst** du **ein**?	Tina: Yes, I need to bring chocolate for my kids. What are you shopping for?
Klaus: Wir **bekommen** morgen Besuch. Deshalb **kaufe** ich viel **ein**. **Komm** doch auch **vorbei**!	Klaus: We are having guests tomorrow. That's why I'm buying lots of things. You should come by, too.
Tina: Danke! Ich werde es mir **überlegen**!	Tina: Thank you! I will think about it!

GERMAN VERB	ENGLISH	GERMAN VERB	ENGLISH
einkaufen	(to) buy, (to) go shopping	vorbeikommen	(to) come by, (to) drop by
mitbringen	(to) bring (along)	überlegen	(to) consider, (to) think about

GENERAL VOCABULARY	ENGLISH	GENERAL VOCABULARY	ENGLISH
Hallo [interj.]	Hi, Hello	was [pron.]	what
Na [interj.]	So, ... ; Well, ...	morgen [adv.]	tomorrow
meinen [pron. Dat.]	(for) my	(der) Besuch [n.]	visitors, guests
(die) Kinder [n. pl.]	children, kids	deshalb [adv.]	therefore
(die) Schokolade [n]	chocolate	viel [pron.]	much, a lot
doch [part.]	*particle for emphasis*	Danke [part.]	thank you

4.1 VERBEN MIT TRENNBAREM PRÄFIX
VERBS WITH SEPARABLE PREFIX

As mentioned above, German verbs with separable prefixes are similar to English phrasal verbs such as "(to) take off", "(to) get up", or "(to) write down". They are separable words functioning as a unit with the verb.

She gets up at 7 o'clock.

phrasal verb, conveying the idea of "leaving bed"

In German, **separable-prefix verbs** can have prefixes such as: *ab-, an-, auf-, aus-, bei-, ein-, fort-, her-, hin-, mit-, nach-, um-, vor-, vorbei-, weg-, weiter-, zurück-,* or *zusammen-*. Looking at two examples from the above dialogue, we can see how these prefixes can be separated from the verb.

Infinitive	Example
einkaufen	*Ich **kaufe** viel **ein**.*
to buy	I am buying a lot of things.
vorbeikommen	***Komm** doch auch **vorbei**!*
to come by	You should come by, too.

In main clauses, separable verbs separate in the two simple tenses (simple present and simple past). The split-off prefix usually goes at the **end of the sentence** in that case.

Another feature of separable verbs is the position of the **ge-** in the **past participle**. Verbs with separable prefixes form the past participle by putting the *ge-* in between the prefix and the past participle form of the verb:

ge- in the middle position

*Ich habe heute noch nicht ein- **ge** -kauft.*

Past Participle of *einkaufen* ('gone shopping')

When using the **imperative** form, the prefix is also separated from the base verb and positioned at the end:

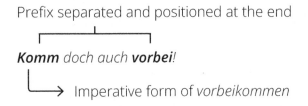

Prefix separated and positioned at the end

Komm *doch auch* **vorbei***!*

Imperative form of *vorbeikommen*

Similarly, **questions** also require the prefix to be separated from the base verb and to be put at the end of the sentence:

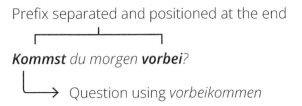

Prefix separated and positioned at the end

Kommst *du morgen* **vorbei***?*

Question using *vorbeikommen*

Furthermore, there are many instances where a verb can take more than just one prefix. The meaning of the newly formed verb will then change according to the prefix used. To provide you with an example, the following list gives you an array of different meanings that the verb *kommen* can assume when combined with different prefixes:

GERMAN VERB	ENGLISH	GERMAN VERB	ENGLISH
abkommen	(to) deviate	mitkommen	(to) come along
aufkommen	(to) arise, (to) emerge	nachkommen	(to) come along later
ankommen	(to) arrive	umkommen	(to) perish
auskommen	(to) get along	unterkommen	(to) find accommodation
durchkommen	(to) pull through	vorkommen	(to) occur
loskommen	(to) get away	wegkommen	(to) break free
herkommen	(to) come here	zurückkommen	(to) come back
hinkommen	(to) get to	zusammenkommen	(to) come together

If you know what the prefix and the base verb mean individually, it is often possible to guess the meaning of the prefix-verb combination, even if you have never come across it before. Please note that this does not work all the time, though, and the meanings of separable-prefix verbs still need to be learned.

👍 DENK DARAN!

You can easily identify if a prefix is separable by looking at the pronunciation of the verb in the infinitive. Almost all verbs with separable prefixes are pronounced with a stress on the prefix or one syllable of the prefix:

ein-kaufen (sep.)
vor**bei**-kommen (sep.)

VS:

be-**kom**men (insep.)

4.2 VERBEN MIT UNTRENNBAREM PRÄFIX
VERBS WITH INSEPARABLE PREFIX

German verbs with **inseparable** prefixes function as **one word** since the prefixes are never separated from the base verb. Some examples of inseparable prefixes include *be-, emp-, ent-, er-, ge-, miss-, über-, ver-,* and *zer-*.

Infinitive	Example
*be*kommen to get / to have	*Wir **bekommen** morgen Besuch.* We are having guests tomorrow.
*über*legen to consider	*Ich werde es mir **überlegen**.* I will consider it.

Inseparable-prefix verbs behave like normal verbs. However, note that they do **not take the *ge-*** in forming the **past participle**, neither at the beginning of the verb, nor in between the prefix and the base verb:

Gestern haben wir Besuch   **bekommen.**   ⟶   Past participles
Ich habe es mir   **überlegt.**   without *ge-*

The following verbs with inseparable prefixes are very common:

GERMAN VERB	ENGLISH	GERMAN VERB	ENGLISH
beantworten	(to) answer (a question)	gebrauchen	(to) utilize
besuchen	(to) visit	missverstehen	(to) misunderstand
bezahlen	(to) pay	missbrauchen	(to) abuse
entgehen	(to) escape	verdienen	(to) earn
empfangen	(to) receive	verkaufen	(to) sell
erleben	(to) experience	verlaufen	(to) proceed, (to) take place
erkennen	(to) recognize	verschlafen	(to) oversleep
erzählen	(to) tell	verstehen	(to) understand
entdecken	(to) discover	zerbrechen	(to) break apart
gewinnen	(to) win, (to) gain	zerstören	(to) destroy

ÜBUNGEN
EXERCISES

 Ü 4.1) Each of the verbs below has a prefix — some of them separable, some inseparable. Listen to their pronunciation and add the verbs to the appropriate column in the table, based on your knowledge of how to recognize each category. Lastly, provide the past participle for each of them.

einschlafen, gestehen, anziehen, umsehen, verlieren, zumachen, befolgen, verachten, weggehen, verhaften, aufhören, empfehlen

SEPARABLE	INSEPARABLE	PAST PARTICIPLE

Ü 4.2) Using a good (online) dictionary, try to find as many prefix — verb combinations as you can, based on the word *sehen*. Hint: There are at least 30 verbs with *sehen* as their base verb.

_____

_____

_____

_____

_____

_____

Ü 4.3) Form complete sentences using the given elements. Be sure to only separate the verbs from their prefixes where appropriate. One example has been done for you.

Example:

ich / vorbeikommen / heute / um 8 Uhr $\longrightarrow$ Ich komme heute um 8 Uhr vorbei.

a) was / du / einkaufen ?

_____

b) ich / gestern / verschlafen .

_____

c) Peter, / aufräumen / dein Zimmer !

_____

d) Klaus, / bezahlen / deine Miete !

_____

e) verkaufen / du / dein Haus ?

_____

f) erkennen / du / ihn ?

_____

g) zurückgeben / mir / mein Buch !

_____

KAPITEL 5 — ÜBERBLICK ÜBER DIE DEUTSCHEN ZEITEN
CHAPTER 5 - OVERVIEW OF THE GERMAN TENSES

Both in German and in English, the **tense** of a verb identifies the point in time at which the action takes place. Essentially, any action can occur in the **present**, the **past**, or in the **future** and verbs are able to reflect this accordingly.

Even though there is some overlap between English and German in the formation and usage of the different tenses, tenses with the same name are not always used in the same way. In this chapter we are going to familiarize you with the **six different German tenses** and their basic uses. Please note that each tense will be discussed in more detail in Unit 2 and that this chapter only serves to prime you for that.

 Take a look at the following example sentences, which feature two sentences for each German tense:

Ich **heiße** *Klaus.* *Ich* **fahre** *häufig mit dem Zug.*	My name is Klaus. (lit. I am called Klaus) I frequently take the train.
Die Frau **besuchte** *ihren Bruder.* *Das Telefon* **klingelte**.	The woman visited her brother. The phone rang.
Ich **habe** *einen Flug* **gebucht**. *Herr Müller* **ist gestorben**.	I (have) booked a flight. Mr. Müller (has) died.
Meine Schwester **war** *vor ihrer Hochzeit schon einmal verheiratet* **gewesen**. *Letzte Woche gingen meine Frau und ich ins Kino, aber ich* **hatte** *den Film schon* **gesehen**.	My sister had already been married once before her wedding. Last week, my wife and I went to the theater, but I had already seen the movie.
Ich **werde** *im Sommer nach Spanien* **fahren**. *Du* **wirst** *diesen Film sicher* **kennen**.	I will go to Spain this summer. You (will) surely know this movie.
Wenn du uns nächstes Jahr besuchst, **wird** *er die Schule* **abgeschlossen haben**. *Sie* **wird** *wohl* **vergessen haben**, *anzurufen.*	When you visit us next year, he will have graduated from school. She probably forgot to call.

GERMAN VERB	ENGLISH	GERMAN VERB	ENGLISH
heißen klingeln arbeiten buchen	(to) be called (to) ring (to) work (to) book	kennen abschließen	(to) know, (to) be familiar with (to) finish, (to) complete; here: (to) graduate

GENERAL VOCABULARY	ENGLISH	GENERAL VOCABULARY	ENGLISH
häufig [adj.] (der) Zug [n.] (die) Frau [n.] ihren [pron. Acc.] (der) Bruder [n.] (das) Telefon [n.] ganz [adj.] (der) Flug [n.] (die) Schwester [n.] vor [prep.] (die) Hochzeit [n.] schon [adv.] einmal [adv.] verheiratet [adj.]	frequently train woman; wife her brother phone whole, entire flight sister before, prior wedding already once married	letzte /-r /-s [adj.] und [conj.] ins [prep.] (das) Kino [n.] (der) Film [n.] (der) Sommer [n.] Spanien [n.] sicher [adv.] wenn [conj.] (das) Jahr [n.] diese /-r /-es [pron.] (die) Zeit [n.] (die) Schule [n.]	last and to the theater, cinema movie, film summer Spain surely when; if year this time school

5.1 DIE SECHS DEUTSCHEN ZEITEN
THE SIX GERMAN TENSES

As already mentioned, actions and events can either take place at the very moment of speaking (**present tense**), or they occurred prior to the moment of speaking (**past tense**), or they are expected to occur at a later point (**future tense**).

These three basic tenses are referred to as *Präsens*, *Präteritum*, and *Futur I* in German. Each of these tenses has a complimentary tense which expresses anteriority, i.e., it describes an action or event that took place prior to the one in the *Präsens*, the *Präteritum*, or the *Futur I*. Those complimentary tenses are called *Perfekt*, *Plusquamperfekt*, and *Futur II* in German.

It is important to be mindful of these complimentary tenses and their relationship to the *Präsens*, *Präteritum* and *Futur I* tenses. They help us express the correct sequence of events and serve to clarify which of the actions occurred earlier and which ones later, especially in more complex sentence structures. Let us have a look at the following timeline:

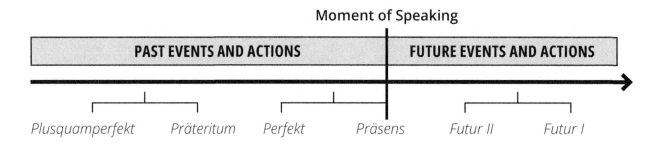

As you can see, all six tenses have been lined up in their chronological sequence in the above timeline. Thus, if we wanted to talk about an action or event that occurred before an action or event in the *Präteritum*, for instance, we would have to choose the *Plusquamperfekt*. For actions prior to the *Präsens* we would choose the *Perfekt* tense, and so forth. To illustrate these time relationships a bit more we will now take a brief look at each of the tenses individually and draw comparisons to their English counterparts.

5.2 DAS PRÄSENS
THE PRESENT TENSE

USAGE	EXAMPLES	COMPARISON TO ENGLISH
• For actions that are taking place right now • For habitual, repeated actions or states of affairs • For actions that started in the past but are still ongoing	*Ich **gehe** jetzt nach Hause.* → Action takes place now *Ich **fahre** häufig mit dem Zug.* → Habitual action Ich **heiße** Klaus. → State of affairs *Er **arbeitet** seit zwei Jahren bei dieser Firma.* → Action began in the past and is still taking place	• Largely the same usage as the simple present • There is no present progressive in German

The *Präsens* is very similar in usage to the English simple present, with the exception that there is **no present progressive** tense in German. If an emphasis on the ongoing nature of an action is required, a time expression such as *gerade* (just) or *im Augenblick* (at present) is often added to the sentence. Furthermore, the *Präsens* can be used to express actions that started in the past and are still ongoing, again often in conjunction with a relevant time expression. In English, the present perfect tense would be required in such an instance.

5.3 DAS PERFEKT
THE PERFECT TENSE

USAGE	EXAMPLES	COMPARISON TO ENGLISH
• To express anteriority in relation to the present	*Wenn du* **angekommen bist**, *essen wir.* → Arrival comes before dining	• Same usage as the present perfect regarding recently completed actions
• To express past actions and events	*Ich* **habe** *einen Flug* **gebucht**. → Booking was made at some point in the past	• The German Perfekt is closer in usage to the English simple past than to the present perfect
• To express an action that has recently been completed	*Ich* **habe** *den Film kürzlich* **gesehen**. → The film has been watched (recently)	• There is no present perfect continuous in German

The German **Perfekt** is a **compound tense** and is therefore not exactly parallel to the English present perfect. In general, its usage is more flexible than that of the English present perfect and it is often called the '**conversational past**', as most past actions are expressed with it in spoken German. It can be used to describe actions that started in the past and just recently concluded, but there is no progressive form to mark it as still ongoing in the present. The *Präsens*, together with a time indication, would be used in such an instance.

5.4 DAS PRÄTERITUM
THE SIMPLE PAST

USAGE	EXAMPLES	COMPARISON TO ENGLISH
• To talk about actions that are completed and in the past • More common in written German and literary texts	*Die Frau* **besuchte** *ihren Bruder.* → The visit took place and finished in the past *Es* **war** *einmal mitten im Winter, und die Schneeflocken* **fielen** *wie Federn vom Himmel herab.* (Beginning of 'Snow White') → Literary text	• Mostly the same usage as the English simple past • Not as common as the English simple past

The **Präteritum** (also referred to as '*Imperfekt*' in German) is one of the less commonly used German tenses. However, it is important to know about it and recognize a verb in this tense. Many literary texts, such as stories and novels, as well as scientific and formally written texts make frequent use of the *Präteritum*. Furthermore, some auxiliary and modal verbs require to be used in the *Präteritum* when forming certain compound tenses. The formation is different for weak and strong verbs and there is again no continuous form of this tense in German.

5.5 DAS PLUSQUAMPERFEKT
THE PAST PERFECT

USAGE	EXAMPLES	COMPARISON TO ENGLISH
• To talk about actions that took place before another action in the past	*Meine Schwester* **war** *vor ihrer Hochzeit schon einmal verheiratet* **gewesen**. → The sister had already been married prior to getting married a second time *Letzte Woche gingen meine Frau und ich ins Kino, aber ich* **hatte** *den Film schon gesehen.* → Speaker had already seen the movie prior to last week's visit to the theater	• Same usage, though sequence of tenses tends to be more strictly observed in German

The **Plusquamperfekt**, another compound tense, is one of the tenses whose formation requires familiarity with the *Präteritum*. It is used to express actions that took place before another action in the past. Its usage is the same in both English and German, but German tends to be somewhat stricter about employing it to convey the accurate sequence of events. In conversation, and if it is clear which action came first, English sometimes uses the simple past to describe an action that preceded another in the past. This is not correct in German.

5.6 DAS FUTUR I
THE FUTURE TENSE

USAGE	EXAMPLES	COMPARISON TO ENGLISH
• To express what will happen in the future • To express what can be expected or assumed to happen • Often replaced by the Präsens in spoken German	*Ich **werde** im Sommer nach Spanien **fahren**.* → Upcoming trip to Spain *Du **wirst** diesen Film sicher **kennen**.* → It is assumed that the other person will know the movie	• Same usage as the "will-future" (also referred to as the "simple future") in English • There is no equivalent construction to the English "going-to" future in German

The **Futur I** is a compound tense whose formation and usage are very similar to the English "will-future". More often than not, especially in spoken German, the *Präsens* is used instead of the *Futur I*. This is because time indications such as *morgen*, *nächstes Jahr* or *später* may already mark the action as taking place in the future. Thus, the above example sentence could also correctly be rendered as *"Im Sommer fahre ich nach Spanien"*. Additionally, the *Futur I* can be used to express a probable fact or what the speaker feels is probably true. This is referred to as the **future of probability**, which does exist in English, but in a much narrower set of expressions. An equivalent construction to the English "going-to future" does not exist in German.

5.7 DAS FUTUR II
THE FUTURE PERFECT

USAGE	EXAMPLES	COMPARISON TO ENGLISH
• To express an action that will have been completed before another action in the future • To express actions that probably took place in the past	*Wenn du uns nächstes Jahr besuchst,* **wird** *er die Schule* **abgeschlossen haben**. → School graduation before the visit next year *Sie* **wird** *wohl* **vergessen haben**, *anzurufen.* → It is probable that she forgot to call	• Same usage as the English future perfect

The **Futur II** is used in exactly the same way as the future perfect in English, i.e., to indicate an action or event that will have taken place before another event in the future. Note how in the timeline in 5.1 the *Futur II* is closer to the moment of speaking than the *Futur I*. Further, the *Futur II* can be used to express events that have probably taken place in the past. This is analogous to the application of the **future of probability** for the *Futur I*, whereas with the *Futur II* the probability concerns the past. The *Futur II* is not used very often and is frequently replaced by the *Perfekt*. Thus, an acceptable way of rephrasing the above example sentence would be *"Wenn du uns nächstes Jahr besuchst, hat er die Schule abgeschlossen."*

ÜBUNGEN
EXERCISES

Ü 5.1) Arrange the following tenses in the right chronological order and match the German and English counterparts.

Futur I; Plusquamperfekt; Present perfect; Future perfect; Präteritum; Futur II; Präsens; Future tense; Simple past; Present tense; Perfekt; Past perfect

_____

_____

_____

_____

Ü 5.2) There is no German continuous form for the present tense. What would you do to emphasize that an action in the *Präsens* is ongoing?

_____

_____

_____

_____

Ü 5.3) Which of the German tenses are compound tenses?

_____

_____

_____

_____

Ü 5.4) Identify the tenses in the following sentences. You may use a dictionary if you are unsure about some of the words used.

Tense

a) Sie hört gerade Musik.   _____

b) In drei Tagen werden wir in den Urlaub fahren.   _____

c) Er hat immer Musik gehört.   _____

d) Früher ist sie oft ins Schwimmbad gegangen.   _____

e) Es war einmal ein reicher König.   _____

f) Sie wird uns wohl nicht gehört haben.   _____

g) Wir hatten uns seit zehn Jahren nicht gesehen.   _____

h) Kommst du aus Deutschland?   _____

i) Er wird wahrscheinlich zuhause sein.   _____

j) Wenn du uns besuchst, werden wir schon
umgezogen sein.   _____

k) Letzte Woche flog ich nach New York.   _____

l) Nachdem er zuhause angekommen war,
kochte er Kaffee.   _____

KAPITEL 6 — DIE DEUTSCHE WORTSTELLUNG
CHAPTER 6 - WORD ORDER IN GERMAN

English tends to rely mostly on **word order** to indicate the grammatical function of a word or phrase. Consider the sentence: "The old man the ship". This so-called garden-path sentence may look confusing at first, but does make sense when deciphered using the traditional English word order of '**Subject-Verb-Object**'. By identifying "man" as a verb (in the sense of "to run/to operate") and not a noun we quickly realize that "it is the old who man the ship".

In the German equivalent sentence "Die Alten bemannen das Schiff", we do not have to deal with this difficulty and the meaning is immediately clear. This has to do with the fact that German relies more on **inflections to show function**. Consequently, endings, such as those indicating the different cases in different genders, or the endings for verb conjugations allow for some greater flexibility in the construction of a sentence. However, this is not to say that there are no rules governing German word order. On the contrary, the way a German sentence is constructed and organized has great bearing on its meaning and much of this inherent organization revolves around the verb of the sentence. In this chapter, we aim to shed some light on the basic rules surrounding this.

 Let us look at the following example sentences:

Ich schlafe.	I am sleeping.
Es regnet.	It is raining.
Das Wasser kocht.	The water is boiling.
Dieses Haus gehört meinem Vermieter.	This house belongs to my landlord.
Er benutzt einen Computer.	He uses a computer.
Der Mann kocht das Abendessen.	The man is cooking dinner.
Peter gibt seinem Freund einen Rat.	Peter gives his friend some advice. (lit. 'an advice')
Er stellt den Motor ab.	He switches the engine off.
Peter möchte sein Haus renovieren.	Peter would like to renovate his house.
Ich habe ein Jobangebot bekommen.	I have received a job offer.
Das Gesetz wird nächstes Jahr geändert.	The law will be amended next year.

GERMAN VERB	ENGLISH	GERMAN VERB	ENGLISH
schlafen	(to) sleep	geben	(to) give
regnen	(to) rain	abstellen	(to) switch off
kochen	(to) boil; (to) cook	renovieren	(to) renovate,
gehören	(to) belong to		(to) refurbish
benutzen	(to) use	ändern	(to) change, (to) amend

GENERAL VOCABULARY	ENGLISH	GENERAL VOCABULARY	ENGLISH
(das) Wasser [*n.*]	water	(der/die) Freund/-in [*n.*]	friend
(das) Haus [*n.*]	house	(der) Rat [*n.*]	advice
(der/die) Vermieter/-in [*n.*]	landlord	(der) Motor [*n.*]	engine
(der) Computer [*n.*]	computer	(das) Jobangebot [*n.*]	job offer
(der) Mann [*n.*]	man	(das) Gesetz [*n.*]	law
(das) Abendessen [*n.*]	dinner		

6.1 DAS PRÄDIKAT UND SEINE BEDEUTUNG FÜR DEN SATZBAU
THE PREDICATE AND ITS IMPORTANCE FOR SENTENCE STRUCTURE

The **predicate** of a sentence contains the conjugated form of the verb. It is the most important building block in a sentence and serves as the axis around which all the other parts of a sentence revolve. A sentence without a predicate is thus an incomplete sentence.

The shortest complete sentences we can build only require two components: a **subject** (i.e., the part of the sentence that is carrying out the action) and a **predicate (verb)**. The predicate may consist of only a verb without any other elements. However, it may also appear in more complex forms, especially in German. In a declarative sentence, its most basic form contains a finite verb, i.e., the one that is conjugated according to the subject:

SUBJECT	PREDICATE
1	2
Ich (I)	*schlafe* (am sleeping).
Wir (We)	*schlafen* (are sleeping).
Es (It)	*regnet* (is raining).

Whether or not a sentence also requires an **object** (i.e., the part of the sentence that receives the action) to make the sentence sound complete and meaningful is dependent on the predicate as well. In German, such objects can appear in different **cases**, such as dative, accusative, or genitive, which the predicate dictates. For instance, the verb *gehören* (to belong) requires a dative object, whereas the verb *benutzen* (to use) needs to be followed by an accusative object:

SUBJECT	PREDICATE	OBJECT
1	2	3
Dieses Haus (This house)	*gehört* (belongs to)	*meinem Vermieter. (Dat.)* (my landlord).
Er (He)	*benutzt* (uses)	*einen Computer. (Acc.)* (a computer).

Both of the above sentences would be incomplete without their respective objects. Unlike *schlafen* or *regnen*, both predicates require an **object** that indicates 'to whom' the house belongs and 'what' is being used by 'him'. Some German verbs may even require **two objects**, while other verbs change their meaning, based on whether or not they require an object:

SUBJECT	PREDICATE	OBJECT	OBJECT
1	2	3	4
Peter (Peter)	*gibt* (gives)	*seinem Freund (Dat.)* (his friend)	*einen Rat. (Acc.)* (some advice).

SUBJECT	PREDICATE	OBJECT
1	2	3
Das Wasser (The water)	*kocht.* (is boiling).	-
Der Mann (The man)	*kocht* (is cooking)	*das Abendessen. (Acc.)* (dinner).

We would now like to direct your attention to the position of the predicate (the verb) in each of the above tables. As you can see, the verb is in the second position in each of the examples. This is one of the most fundamental rules concerning German word order. While other elements, such as the subject or the object, can sometimes move position, the predicate almost always **takes the 2nd position** in declarative sentences. Therefore, we can establish the following formula for simple declarative statements in which the predicate consists of one word:

1	2	3
Subject	**Predicate (Verb)**	Object(s)

6.2 DIE SATZKLAMMER
THE SENTENCE BRACKET

The predicate does not always consist of just one word. There are **modal verbs** that modify the main verb, **auxiliary verbs** that form tenses with other verbs, **separable prefix verbs**, and there are **verbal phrases** consisting of a verb and another element. Predicates that are composed of several parts in this manner are split up and embrace other parts of the sentence, which is sometimes referred to as a **sentence bracket**:

SUBJECT	PREDICATE (1ST PART)	OBJECT OR ADVERBIAL PHRASE	PREDICATE (2ND PART)
1	2	3	4
Er (He)	stellt (switches)	den Motor (Acc.) (the engine)	ab (off)
Peter (Peter)	möchte (would like to)	sein Haus (Acc.) (his house)	renovieren. (renovate)
Ich (I)	habe (have)	ein Jobangebot (a job offer)	bekommen (received)
Das Gesetz (The law)	wird (will be)	nächstes Jahr (next year)	geändert. (amended)

Sentence Bracket

All parts of a sentence bracket make up the predicate. There can be up to four parts to the predicate in more complex tense constructions, such as the passive subjunctive of the *Plusquamperfekt*:

Er **hätte** schon längst **gefeuert werden müssen**.

(He should have been fired a long time ago.)

The important thing to note, however, is that the **conjugated** part of the predicate ("*hätte*" in the above sentence) is again in the **2nd position**, regardless of how many parts the predicate consists of. The subject and object of a sentence may sometimes be put in different positions, often in order to achieve a shift in emphasis, but the **conjugated (finite)** part of the predicate nearly always stays in the 2nd position. The **non-finite parts of the predicate** (e.g., the past participle of the perfect tense or passive, the infinitive of the future tense, split-up prefixes etc.) go at the end in a declarative sentence. Consequently, we may expand our formula from section 6.1 to the following:

1	2	3	4
Subject	Conjugated (finite) part of the Predicate	Object(s) or adverbial phrase	Unconjugated (non-finite) part of the Predicate

A common deviation from this formula occurs when the subject and the object or adverbial phrase swap position, which can be done to change emphasis. The position of the **predicate remains unaffected** by this:

OBJECT OR ADVERBIAL PHRASE	PREDICATE (1ST PART)	SUBJECT	PREDICATE (2ND PART)
1	2	3	4
Nächtes Jahr	wird	das Gesetz	geändert.
Sein Haus	möchte	Peter	renovieren.

Declarative statements can be **negated** using the word **nicht** (not). *Nicht* never changes form, but it can appear in different positions within a sentence: It usually comes **after** the conjugated part of the predicate and the object or adverbial expression of definite time ('*nächstes Jahr*'). However, it goes **before** most other adverbs and adverbs expressing general time (e.g., '*oft*').

1	2	3	4	5
Das Gesetz	*wird*	*nächstes Jahr*	**nicht**	*geändert.*
Peter	*möchte*	*sein Haus*	**nicht**	*renovieren.*
Er	*benutzt*	**nicht**	*oft*	*einen Computer.*

6.3 WORTSTELLUNG IN FRAGEN
WORD ORDER IN QUESTIONS

Just like in English, there are two types of questions in German: 'yes-or-no questions' and 'W-questions' (*who, where, what, when, why,* etc.).

Yes-or-no questions are formed by inverting the word order of the subject and the verb. This means, the conjugated part of the predicate moves from its second position in a statement to the first position and it is followed by the subject:

1	2	3	4	5
Wird	**das Gesetz**	*nächstes Jahr*	*geändert?*	
Möchte	**Peter**	*sein Haus*	*nicht*	*renovieren?*
Gibt	**Peter**	*seinem Freund*	*einen Rat?*	

In **W-questions** (*Wer, Was, Wann, Warum, Wo, Wie,* etc.), the question word is usually positioned at the beginning of the sentence. It is followed by the conjugated part of the predicate and the subject, using the same word order as above:

1	2	3	4	5
Wann	*wird*	*das Gesetz*	*geändert?*	
Warum	*möchte*	*Peter*	*sein Haus*	*renovieren?*
Wie	*kocht*	*der Mann*	*das Abendessen?*	

As we have seen, in the majority of cases the conjugated part of the predicate remains in the second position of the sentence, while the non-finite part of the predicate moves to the end of the sentence. Questions (and commands, which will be discussed in Unit 3) are the only exception to this rule since they require the predicate to take the first position followed by the subject.

One could go into a lot more detail about the German word order, especially regarding the construction of subclauses. This, however, would go beyond the scope of this chapter. Relevant concepts in this regard will be introduced and explained at appropriate points later in this book.

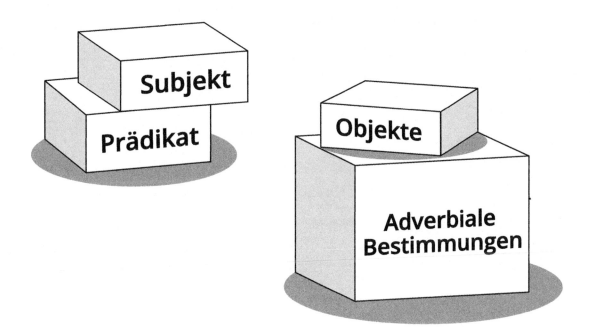

ÜBUNGEN
EXERCISES

Ü 6.1) Have a look at the following sentences and label the subject, the predicate, and the object(s) in each of them. Bear in mind that there may be several parts to the predicate in some instances (consisting of an accusative or dative object, or even both).

a) Anna kocht das Abendessen.

_____

b) Sie gibt ihrem Freund ein Geschenk.

_____

c) Das Haus wird nächstes Jahr gebaut werden.

_____

d) Letztes Jahr hat Peter geheiratet.

_____

e) Die Miete können wir inzwischen nicht mehr bezahlen.

_____

f) Kannst du deinem Freund Geld geben?

_____

Ü 6.2) Each of the following sentences contains one mistake relating to the correct word order. Find the mistake and correct it.

a) Die Schüler ein Buch lesen.

_____

b) Werden nächstes Jahr wir ein Haus bauen?

_____

c) Warum möchte Lisa ihrem Freund geben einen Rat?

_____

d) Nächste Woche wir verkaufen unser Auto einem Freund.

_____

Ü 6.3) Use the following elements to form as many correct and meaningful sentences as you can.

der Mann	bauen	dem Freund	kochen	das Auto
ihr	wir	nächstes Jahr	das Abendessen	warum
ist	sind	kocht	wie	kaufen
gekauft	geben	haben	ein Haus	gegeben

_____

_____

_____

_____

_____

_____

_____

_____

_____

_____

_____

_____

Unit 2

TENSES

Having covered a variety of foundational concepts in Unit 1 regarding the different types of verbs, verb tenses, and particularities of German verbs, **Unit 2** will provide you with a more detailed look at the German **verb tenses**. In general, most German verb tenses are no more difficult or complex to understand and master than the English verb tenses. In a sense, they are even easier to apply in practice as German allows for a more flexible use of tenses in certain situations. Nevertheless, there are distinct usage scenarios and a logical structure to each of the German tenses. This is what the following chapters will look at and explain for each tense individually.

KAPITEL 7 — DAS PRÄSENS
CHAPTER 7 - THE PRESENT TENSE

The **Präsens** is one of the most frequently used tenses in German. Not only does it serve to talk about things that are currently happening, but it can even be used to express future events. In this chapter, we will explain its usage and formation in detail.

 First, however, let us have a look at the following dialogue between David and Bernd. They both just started college and are introducing themselves to each other during their first class together:

David: Hi, ich **heiße** David. **Bist** du auch ein Ersti?	David: Hi, my name is David. Are you a freshman as well?
Bernd: Servus, ich **bin** Bernd. Ja, das hier **ist** meine erste Vorlesung. Woher **kommst** du?	Bernd: Hey, I'm Bernd. Yes, this is my first lecture. Where are you from?
David: Meine Familie **kommt** aus Hamburg, aber ich **lebe** seit einem Jahr hier in München. **Sollen** wir gemeinsam einen Kaffee trinken? Ich **habe** nachher frei.	David: My family is from Hamburg, but I have been living here in Munich for one year. Shall we go for coffee together? I'll be free later.
Bernd: Ja, das **können** wir gern machen. Wir **sehen** uns nach der Vorlesung!	Bernd: Yes, I'd love to do that. See you after the lecture!

GERMAN VERB	ENGLISH	GERMAN VERB	ENGLISH
herkommen	(to) come from	freihaben	(to) be free / off
leben	(to) live	machen	(to) do; (to) make
trinken	(to) drink		

GENERAL VOCABULARY	ENGLISH	GENERAL VOCABULARY	ENGLISH
hi [*interj.*]	hi, hello	(die) Familie [*n.*]	family
(der) Ersti [*n.*] [*coll.*]	first-semester student;	aus [*prep.*]	from; out of
	freshman	seit [*prep.*]	since
Servus [*interj.*]	a greeting, especially	ein /-e [*adj.*]	one
	common in southern	in [*prep.*]	in
	Germany and Austria	nachher [*adv.*]	afterwards, later
das hier [*pron.*]	this here	gemeinsam [*adj.*]	jointly, together
erste /-r /-s [*adj.*]	first	(der) Kaffee [*n.*]	coffee
(die) Vorlesung [*n.*]	(university) lecture	gern [*adv.*]	gladly
woher [*adv.*]	where from	gern machen [*idiom*]	(to) love to do

7.1 DIE KONSTRUKTION DES PRÄSENS
CONSTRUCTING THE PRESENT TENSE

In Chapter 1 of Unit 1 we already mentioned that there are **regular** (weak) and **irregular** (strong) verbs in German. While this distinction will become especially important as we discuss the *Perfekt* and the *Präteritum*, it also has an impact on the way we form the *Präsens* in German. Let us first have a look at the way regular verbs form the *Präsens*.

7.1.1 Regular Verbs

As you know, the infinitive ending for all German verbs is either '-*en*' or '-*n*'. In order to conjugate a verb, we need to separate the infinitive ending from the verb stem and replace it with the appropriate **finite ending**. The required ending is determined by the **subject** of the sentence, i.e., by the person, animal, thing, concept, etc. that carries out the action of the verb (also called the 'grammatical person'). There are three grammatical persons each for the singular and plural. Thus, the following table shows the German present-tense endings, using the regular verb '*leben*' as an example:

	ENDING	EXAMPLE		ENGLISH	
1st person (sing.)	*-e*	*ich*	*lebe*	I	live
2nd person (sing.)	*-st*	*du*	*lebst*	you	live
3rd person (sing.)	*-t*	*er/sie/es*	*lebt*	he/she/it	lives
1st person (pl.)	*-en*	*wir*	*leben*	we	live
2nd person (pl.)	*-t*	*ihr*	*lebt*	you	live
3rd person (pl.)	*-en*	*sie*	*leben*	they	live
Formal (sing. & pl.)	*-en*	*Sie*	*leben*	you	live

Note that the **formal address** '*Sie*' (with a capitalized 's') is the same for both singular and plural and that it takes the same ending as the 3ʳᵈ person plural. In German, this is the way in which adults who are unfamiliar to you or people of authority are formally addressed. Thus, instead of saying "*Herr Müller, wo lebst du?*" you would ask "*Herr Müller, wo leb**en Sie**?*".

7.1.2 Irregular Verbs

German **irregular verbs** show one peculiarity in the present tense: They undergo a stem vowel change. This applies to those irregular verbs whose stem contains one of the following vowels or diphthongs:

a	becomes	*ä*
e	becomes	*i* or *ie*
au	becomes	*äu*
o	becomes	*ö*

These changes happen in the **2ⁿᵈ** ('*du*') and **3ʳᵈ** ('*er/sie/es*') **person singular** only and they do **not affect the endings**. Take a look at the following table, which lists an example word for each vowel change:

STEM	ICH	DU	ER/SIE/ES
schlafen (to sleep)	*schlafe*	*schläfst*	*schläft*
helfen (to help)	*helfe*	*hilfst*	*hilft*
laufen (to run)	*laufe*	*läufst*	*läuft*
sehen (to see)	*sehe*	*siehst*	*sieht*
stoßen (to push)	*stoße*	*stößt*	*stößt*

There is no hard and fast rule as to whether a verb has a vowel change in the present tense and irregularities of this type must be learned by heart. However, as you gain more exposure to German through reading and listening to native speakers, you will develop a feel for the correct usage. The following list compiles a few more commonly used verbs where a vowel change occurs in the present tense:

VOWEL CHANGE	VERBS	2ND AND 3RD PERSON	
a → ä	*fahren* (to drive)	*du fährst*	*er/sie/es fährt*
	halten (to hold)	*du hältst*	*er/sie/es hält*
	tragen (to carry/to wear)	*du trägst*	*er/sie/es trägt*
	waschen (to wash)	*du wäschst*	*er/sie/es wäscht*
	fangen (to catch)	*du fängst*	*er/sie/es fängt*
	schlagen (to beat/to hit)	*du schlägst*	*er/sie/es schlägt*
	wachsen (to grow)	*du wächst*	*er/sie/es wächst*
	lassen (to let/to leave)	*du lässt*	*er/sie/es lässt*
e → i	*sprechen* (to speak)	*du sprichst*	*er/sie/es spricht*
	essen (to eat)	*du isst*	*er/sie/es isst*
	geben (to give)	*du gibst*	*er/sie/es gibt*
	treffen (to meet)	*du triffst*	*er/sie/es trifft*
	werfen (to throw)	*du wirfst*	*er/sie/es wirft*
	vergessen (to forget)	*du vergisst*	*er/sie/es vergisst*
	nehmen (to take)	*du nimmst*	*er/sie/es nimmt*
		(Note the double 'm' spelling variation here!)	
au → äu	*saufen* (to guzzle/to booze)	*du säufst*	*er/sie/es säuft*
e → ie	*empfehlen* (to recommend)	*du empfiehlst*	*er/sie/es empfiehlt*
	stehlen (to steal)	*du stiehlst*	*er/sie/es stiehlt*
	lesen (to read)	*du liest*	*er/sie/es liest*
	befehlen (to command)	*du befiehlst*	*er/sie/es befiehlt*

Note that only a **-t** is added in the 2nd person with verbs whose stem ends in **s**, **ss**, **ß**, or **tz**:

wachs-en	→	*du wächs-**t***
lass-en	→	*du läss-**t***
ess-en	→	*du iss-**t***
vergess-en	→	*du vergiss-**t***
les-en	→	*du lies-**t***

7.1.3 Modal Verbs

In Chapter 2 we already discussed the function and usage of the **six German modal verbs** and provided you with their simple present conjugations. For better continuity, let us review that conjugation table:

	DÜRFEN	**KÖNNEN**	**MÜSSEN**
ich	*darf*	*kann*	*muss*
du	*darfst*	*kannst*	*musst*
er/sie/es	*darf*	*kann*	*muss*
wir	*dürfen*	*können*	*müssen*
ihr	*dürft*	*könnt*	*müsst*
sie/Sie	*dürfen*	*können*	*müssen*
	SOLLEN	**WOLLEN**	**MÖGEN**
ich	*soll*	*will*	*mag*
du	*sollst*	*willst*	*magst*
er/sie/es	*soll*	*will*	*mag*
wir	*sollen*	*wollen*	*mögen*
ihr	*sollt*	*wollt*	*mögt*
sie/Sie	*sollen*	*wollen*	*mögen*

As you can see, the six German modal verbs exhibit extremely **irregular** patterns that do not always follow the vowel change rules outlined in the previous section. These exceptions have to be learned by heart.

You already know that modal verbs change the meaning of the main verb to give it a certain emphasis or 'spin' (→ cf. Ch. 3). The main verb remains in the infinitive, while the modal verb is conjugated as required:

Conjugated modal (1st person, plural)

*Soll**en** wir nachher gemeinsam Kaffee trinken?*

Main verb (infinitive)

7.1.4 Auxiliary Verbs

The German **auxiliary verbs** *haben*, *sein*, and *werden* are important elements in forming **compound tenses** and the **passive voice**, as we learned in Chapter 4. Many of these compound tenses, however, require the auxiliary verb to be conjugated in the present tense, while the main verb appears in the past participle or the infinitive. Let us therefore have a look at the present tense conjugations of the auxiliary verbs:

	SEIN		HABEN		WERDEN	
1st person (sing.)	*ich*	**bin**	*ich*	**habe**	*ich*	**werde**
2nd person (sing.)	*du*	**bist**	*du*	**hast**	*du*	**wirst**
3rd person (sing.)	*er/sie/es*	**ist**	*er/sie/es*	**hat**	*er/sie/es*	**wird**
1st person (pl.)	*wir*	**sind**	*wir*	**haben**	*wir*	**werden**
2nd person (pl.)	*ihr*	**seid**	*ihr*	**habt**	*ihr*	**werdet**
3rd person (pl.)	*sie/Sie*	**sind**	*sie/Sie*	**haben**	*sie/Sie*	**werden**

The German auxiliary verbs, much like the modal verbs, have irregular present tense conjugations. However, it is important to memorize them due to their frequent use.

7.2 DER GEBRAUCH DES PRÄSENS
THE USAGE OF THE PRESENT TENSE

Chapter 5 already gave you an overview of the different uses of the German present tense. We will now have a look at those usage scenarios in some more detail. Thus, we use the *Präsens* in the following instances:

- **To express an ongoing activity or state:**

Das Kind schläft gerade.	(The child is sleeping right now.)
Peter ist krank.	(Peter is ill.)

    → The activity is taking place at the moment. Note that, unlike in English, there is **no present progressive form** in German (e.g., 'the child **is sleeping**'). If the ongoing nature of an activity needs to be emphasized, we may include an adverbial time expression such as *gerade* (right now), *momentan* (currently), or *im Augenblick* (at the moment).

- **For habitual or recurring actions:**

Wir stehen jeden Tag um 7 Uhr auf.	(We get up at 7 o'clock every day.)
Der Zug fährt um 13:30 Uhr ab.	(The train departs at 1:30pm.)

    → The activity takes place regularly or according to schedule. Common signal words to indicate regularity include *immer* (always), *oft* (often), *häufig* (frequently), *selten* (rarely), *nie* (never).

- **To express something that is always true:**

Meine Familie kommt aus Hamburg.	(My family is from Hamburg.)
Die Sonne geht im Osten auf.	(The sun rises in the east.)

    → General truth.

- **For actions that started in the past and are still ongoing:**

Ich lebe seit einem Jahr in München.	(I have been living in Munich for one year.)
Ich arbeite hier seit 2005.	(I have worked here since 2005.)

    → Action started at some point in the past and is still taking place. Note that these scenarios would usually require the present perfect (progressive) tense in English (e.g., 'I **have worked**'). The preposition **seit** is used to indicate both the point at which the action started ('*seit 2005*') as well as the time span during which the action has been going on ('*seit einem Jahr*').

- **For future actions that are planned or have been agreed to:**

Wir sehen uns nach der Vorlesung!   (I'll see you after the lecture!)
Er fährt nächste Woche in den Urlaub.   (He is going on vacation next week.)

→ There is a definite plan or intention to carry out the action. This usage is similar to how the present progressive can be used in English to express a future plan ('He **is going** on vacation'). If the *Präsens* is used to indicate a future action it needs to be clear from either the context or by adding an adverbial time expression that we are talking about the future.

ÜBUNGEN
EXERCISES

Ü 7.1) Fill in the correct present tense verb forms.

a) Hallo, wie _____ (heißen) du?

b) Pedro _____ (kommen) aus Portugal.

c) Er _____ (wohnen) seit zwei Jahren in Berlin.

d) Marlene _____ (sprechen) Spanisch, Chinesisch und Deutsch.

e) Was _____ (studieren) Sie?

f) Frau Meyer _____ (arbeiten) als Anwältin.

g) Ich _____ (lernen) seit einem Jahr Deutsch.

h) Was _____ (sein) Sie von Beruf?

i) _____ (haben) ihr auch Hunger?

j) Die Kinder _____ (spielen) Fußball.

Ü 7.2) Write down the present tense conjugations for the following verbs:

	machen	wollen	treffen	lesen	werden
ich					
du					
er/sie/es					
wir					
ihr					
sie/Sie					

Ü 7.3) Listen to the recording of these 10 verbs. All of them are in the 3rd person singular and are accompanied by the personal pronoun *"er"*. Keep possible vowel changes in mind and write down the infinitive of each verb.

_____

_____

_____

_____

_____

_____

KAPITEL 8 — DAS PERFEKT
CHAPTER 8 - THE PERFECT TENSE

The German **Perfekt** tense, just like the English present perfect, is a frequently used **compound tense**. Although both the German and the English version of this tense share some similarities, it is important to note that they cannot be used in a parallel manner. In this chapter you will learn everything you need to know to form and use the German *Perfekt* with confidence.

 Listen to the following dialogue, in which Karin and Lisa talk about their past weekend activities using the *Perfekt* tense:

Karin: Hallo Lisa, wie geht's?	Karin: Hi Lisa, how are you?
Lisa: Gut, danke! Mein Mann und ich haben letztes Wochenende den Dachboden aufgeräumt. Was habt ihr gemacht?	Lisa: Good, thanks! My husband and I cleaned up the attic last weekend. What did you guys do?
Karin: Am Samstag sind wir auf den Wochenmarkt gegangen. Am Abend haben wir eine leckere Fischpfanne gekocht. Am Sonntag sind wir zu meinen Schwiegereltern gefahren.	Karin: On Saturday, we went to the weekly market. In the evening, we cooked a delicious fish stew. On Sunday, we went to see my parents-in-law.
Lisa: Wie schön! Dann habt ihr ein entspanntes Wochenende gehabt. Wir sind am Sonntagabend sofort eingeschlafen, weil wir so müde waren. Na ja, gute Woche wünsche ich dir! Bis bald!	Lisa: Nice! So, you had a relaxed weekend. We fell asleep immediately on Sunday evening because we were so tired. Oh well, have a good week! See you soon!
Karin: Danke, bis bald!	Karin: Thanks, see you soon!

GERMAN VERB	ENGLISH	GERMAN VERB	ENGLISH
aufräumen kochen	(to) clean/tidy up (to) cook; (to) boil	einschlafen wünschen	(to) fall asleep (to) wish

GENERAL VOCABULARY	ENGLISH	GENERAL VOCABULARY	ENGLISH
wie [adv.]	how	(der) Sonntag [n.]	Sunday
wie geht's? [idiom]	how are you?	(die) Schwiegereltern [n.]	parents-in-law
gut [adj.]	good	schön [adj.]	beautiful, nice
(das) Wochenende [n.]	weekend	dann [adv.]	then; so
(der) Dachboden [n.]	attic	entspannt [adj.]	relaxed
(der) Samstag [n.]	Saturday	sofort [adv.]	immediately
(der) Wochenmarkt [n.]	weekly market	weil [conj.]	because
(der) Abend [n.]	evening	müde [adj.]	tired
lecker [adj.]	delicious, yummy	na ja [interj.]	oh well
(die) Fischpfanne [n.]	fish stew	bis bald [idiom]	see you soon

8.1 DIE KONSTRUKTION DES PERFEKTS
CONSTRUCTING THE PERFECT TENSE

Chapters 1 and 3 of this book (as well as the tenses overview in chapter 5) already provided you with a solid background that allows you to form the German *Perfekt* tense. In the following paragraphs we will bring the relevant elements from those chapters together and go into more detail about the different usage scenarios.

8.1.1 Regular Verbs

The *Perfekt* tense of most **regular** verbs is constructed by using the present tense of the auxiliary verb **haben** together with the **past participle** of the relevant main verb.

	AUXILIARY VERB		PAST PARTICIPLE
Was	*habt*	*ihr*	*gemacht?*
Wir	*haben*	*den Dachboden*	*aufgeräumt.*

As you know, the German past participle of regular verbs is formed by adding the prefix **ge-** and the ending **-t** to the stem of the infinitive. If we want to form the past participle of a verb with a **separable prefix** (such as *aufräumen*), the ge- is added in between the prefix and the stem (thus, *auf - **ge** - räumt*).

Furthermore, do not forget that regular verbs with **inseparable prefix** do **not** take the *ge-* in forming the past participle:

INSEPARABLE PREFIX VERB		AUXILIARY VERB		PAST PARTICIPLE
verkaufen	*Ich*	*habe*	*mein Auto*	*verkauft.*
erzählen	*Sie*	*hat*	*eine Geschichte*	*erzählt.*

8.1.2 Irregular Verbs

The pattern for forming the *Perfekt* tense of regular verbs also applies to **irregular** verbs. One difference is that the past participle of most irregular verbs is formed by putting an **-en** at the end, instead of a *-t*:

	AUXILIARY VERB		PAST PARTICIPLE
Ich	*bin*	*nach Hause*	*gegang**en**.*
Gestern	*haben*	*wir Besuch*	*bekomm**en**.*
Wir	*sind*	*sofort*	*eingeschlaf**en**.*

The rules concerning separable vs. inseparable prefix verbs hold true with irregular verbs as well: No *-ge* is added to the past participle of **inseparable** prefix verbs (*bekommen → bekommen*), while the *ge-* goes in between the prefix and the stem of the **separable** prefix verb in the past participle (*einschlafen → ein-**ge**-schlafen*).

The other difference that irregular verbs show in forming the *Perfekt* tense is their stem vowel change. Much like the stem vowel changes in the 2nd and 3rd person singular of the present tense, many (but not all) irregular verbs undergo a vowel change when forming the past participle:

gehen	→	*geg**a**ngen*	(gone)
bleiben	→	*gebl**ie**ben*	(stayed)
helfen	→	*geh**o**lfen*	(helped)
trinken	→	*getr**u**nken*	(drunk)

Since these vowel changes do not consistently occur with every irregular verb, it is good practice to simply memorize the past participle form of all irregular verbs, together with their infinitive and simple past forms. An extensive list of irregular verbs can be found at the end of this book.

8.1.3 Mixed Verbs

Furthermore, there are verbs called **mixed verbs,** which combine the characteristics of regular and irregular verbs. These are verbs with regular verb endings (i.e., they use the **-t** ending for their past participles), but nevertheless show a vowel change. Some common mixed verbs are:

VERB	ENGLISH		PAST PARTICIPLE	
wissen	(to) know	→	*gewusst*	(known)
denken	(to) think	→	*gedacht*	(thought)
bringen	(to) bring	→	*gebracht*	(brought)
rennen	(to) run	→	*gerannt*	(run)
kennen	(to) know	→	*gekannt*	(known)
nennen	(to) name	→	*genannt*	(named)

8.1.4 When to use *sein* and *haben* as the auxiliary verb

The majority of verbs require **haben** as their auxiliary verb to form the *Perfekt* tense. However, a smaller group of verbs requires the auxiliary verb **sein** to be used instead. Verbs of this category often express **movement** or a **change in condition**. Take a look at these sentences from the dialogue section:

> *Am Samstag sind wir auf den Wochenmarkt gegangen.*
> *Am Sonntag sind wir zu meinen Schwiegereltern gefahren.*

Both of the above sentences use a conjugated form of *sein* as their auxiliary verb, due to the fact that their main verbs are **verbs of movement** (*gehen* and *fahren*).

Another sentence from the dialogue section uses a verb describing a **change of state or condition** and therefore also requires *sein* as the auxiliary verb:

> *Wir sind sofort eingeschlafen.*

Other frequently used verbs that take *sein* as the auxiliary verb because they indicate a **change of state or condition** include:

VERB	ENGLISH	PERFEKT TENSE (3RD PERSON SINGULAR USED AS AN EXAMPLE)	
aufstehen	(to) get up	→	er ist aufgestanden
aufwachen	(to) wake up	→	er ist aufgewacht
sterben	(to) die	→	er ist gestorben
wachsen	(to) grow	→	er ist gewachsen
werden	(to) become	→	er ist geworden

8.2 DAS PERFEKT DER MODAL- UND HILFSVERBEN
THE PERFECT TENSE OF MODAL VERBS AND AUXILIARY VERBS

It is somewhat unusual for the German modal and auxiliary verbs to appear in the *Perfekt* tense. This is even true in spoken language, where the perfect tense is otherwise far more commonly used. Instead, the **simple past** of the required modal or auxiliary verb is often preferable in colloquial speech. Nevertheless, the *Perfekt* does exist for all the modal and auxiliary verbs, and they do surface occasionally. The following tables provide you with an overview of their perfect-tense forms.

		dürfen	können	müssen	sollen	wollen	mögen	haben
ich	habe							
du	hast							
er/ sie/es	hat							
wir	haben	*gedurft*	*gekonnt*	*gemusst*	*gesollt*	*gewollt*	*gemocht*	*gehabt*
ihr	habt							
sie/Sie	haben							

Note that all six modal verbs take '*haben*' as the auxiliary verb. When *haben* is used as a main verb, then it also requires *haben* as an auxiliary verb in the perfect tense. The other two auxiliary verbs, however, take *sein* to form the perfect tense:

		sein	werden
ich	bin		
du	bist		
er/sie/es	ist		
wir	sind	*gewesen*	*geworden*
ihr	seid		
sie/Sie	sind		

As you can see, both *sein* and *werden* have completely irregular past participles.

8.3 DER GEBRAUCH DES PERFEKTS
THE USAGE OF THE PERFECT TENSE

The *Perfekt* is the most commonly used tense to speak about the **past**. In general, and especially as a beginning learner of German, it is always your safest bet to opt for the *Perfekt* when speaking about past events. As you become more proficient, and with growing exposure to the language, you will develop a feel for the subtleties in usage that the different tenses imply. That said, the *Perfekt* tense is primarily used in the following scenarios:

- **To show anteriority in relation to the present tense**

  *Da ich meine Hausaufgaben **erledigt habe**, spiele ich jetzt Fußball.*
  (Since I have completed my homework, I am going to play soccer now.)

  *Er **hat** zu viel **gegessen** und jetzt geht es ihm schlecht.*
  (He ate too much and now he is feeling sick.)

  → Describes **past events** that have **present implications**.

- **To express past actions and events in general**

Letzten Sonntag **sind** *wir nach München* **gefahren.**   (Last Sunday we went to Munich.)
Als Kind **habe** *ich oft* **geweint.**   (I cried a lot as a child.)

→ The action is in the past and does not have a direct relation to the present. Although the German simple past could technically be used in these instances, German speakers almost exclusively use the *Perfekt* tense in **spoken language**. An exception to this are modal and auxiliary verbs, where the simple past would be the more natural choice, as explained in section 8.2.

- **For recently completed actions**

Er **ist** *kürzlich Vater* **geworden.**   (He has recently become a dad.)
Der Zug **ist** *gerade* **abgefahren.**   (The train has just departed.)

→ Recently completed action. The usage of the English present perfect and the German *Perfekt* is very similar in this regard. Common signal words implying recent activity include *soeben* (just), *kürzlich* (recently), *neulich* (the other day), and *vor Kurzem* (not long ago).

ÜBUNGEN
EXERCISES

Ü 8.1) Out of the following list of infinitive verbs, choose the fitting verb for each sentence and fill in the gaps using the past participle.

schlafen, bleiben, beginnen, trinken, essen, anrufen, fahren, ankommen, laufen

a) Wie viele Pfannkuchen hast du _____?

b) Im Urlaub bin ich jeden Tag zwei Kilometer am Strand _____.

c) Guten Morgen! Hast du gut _____?

d) Karin wollte nicht auf die Party gehen. Deshalb ist sie zuhause _____.

e) Ich habe auf der Party zu viel Alkohol _____.

f) Deine Mutter hat vorhin _____. Sie wollte mit dir reden.

g) Wir haben kein Auto. Deshalb sind wir mit dem Zug _____.

h) Ich habe dir einen Brief geschrieben. Ist er schon _____?

i) Schnell! Der Film hat schon _____!

Ü 8.2) Complete the following sentences with the correct auxiliary verb, *haben* or *sein*.

a) Ich _____ nach Hause gegangen.

b) Maria _____ uns gesehen.

c) Ihr _____ Spaghetti gegessen.

d) _____ du um neun Uhr eingeschlafen?

e) _____ ihr gestern Fußball gespielt?

f) Onkel Hans _____ Medizin studiert.

g) _____ ihr zum Taxistand gelaufen?

h) Mein Großvater _____ im Jahr 1995 gestorben.

i) Ich _____ nach München gefahren.

Ü 8.3) The following verbs each have a prefix, some of them separable, some inseparable. Provide the *Perfekt* tense in the 1st and 3rd person singular for each of them, as shown in the example. Be mindful of using the correct auxiliary verb (*sein* or *haben*). Careful: Some of the verbs are irregular!

Example:

einkaufen → ich habe eingekauft | er hat eingekauft

verstehen → ich habe verstanden | er hat verstanden

a) aufwachen

_____

b) besprechen

_____

c) wegfahren

_____

d) versprechen

_____

e) zumachen

_____

f) aufstehen

_____

g) ablegen

_____

h) mitbringen

_____

Ü 8.4) Translate the following sentences into German using the Perfekt tense.

a) Has he gotten up yet?

_____

b) I did not know that.

_____

c) What did you say?

_____

d) Your sister called.

_____

e) I bought a computer.

_____

f) We walked to the weekly market.

_____

g) She flew with Lufthansa.

_____

h) The children have grown.

_____

i) The guests stayed for a long time.

_____

j) The weather has become nice.

_____

KAPITEL 9 — DAS PRÄTERITUM
CHAPTER 9 - THE SIMPLE PAST

The German simple past, called **Präteritum** or *Imperfekt*, is one of the two 'simple' tenses in German (the other one being the *Präsens*). This means that it is not a compound tense and does not require an auxiliary verb like, for example, the *Perfekt* does. However, it is one of the less frequently used tenses, especially in spoken German. This chapter will introduce you to the most important concepts relating to the *Präteritum*.

 The following text is the beginning of the short story *Das Brot* ('The Bread') by German author Wolfgang Borchert (1921 — 1947). In this excerpt, the author makes extensive use of the *Präteritum* tense, and the highlighted verbs indicate this.

*Plötzlich **wachte** sie **auf**. Es **war** halb drei. Sie überlegte, warum sie aufgewacht war. Ach so! In der Küche hatte jemand gegen einen Stuhl gestoßen. Sie **horchte** nach der Küche. Es **war** still. Es **war** zu still und als sie mit der Hand über das Bett neben sich **fuhr**, **fand** sie es leer. Das **war** es, was es so besonders still gemacht hatte: sein Atem **fehlte**. Sie **stand auf** und **tappte** durch die dunkle Wohnung zur Küche. In der Küche **trafen** sie sich. Die Uhr **war** halb drei. Sie **sah** etwas Weißes am Küchenschrank stehen. Sie **machte** Licht. Sie **standen** sich im Hemd **gegenüber**. Nachts. Um halb drei. In der Küche.*	Suddenly she woke up. It was 2:30. She thought about why she had woken up. Oh yes! In the kitchen someone had bumped against a chair. She listened in the direction of the kitchen. It was quiet. It was too quiet, and as she ran her hand over the bed beside her, she found it empty. That's what it was, that's what had made it so especially quiet: his breathing was missing. She got up and groped her way through the dark apartment to the kitchen. In the kitchen they met. The time was 2:30. She saw something white standing by the kitchen cabinet. She turned on the light. They stood facing each other in their shirts. At night. At 2:30. In the kitchen.

GERMAN VERB	ENGLISH	GERMAN VERB	ENGLISH
stoßen	(to) bump; (to) shove	tappen	(to) tiptoe, (to) walk hesitantly
horchen	(to) listen (for smth.)		
fahren	*here:* (to) run one's hand over	(sich) treffen	(to) meet (each other)
finden	(to) find	gegenüberstehen	(to) face (each other)
fehlen	(to) be missing; (to) lack		

GENERAL VOCABULARY	ENGLISH	GENERAL VOCABULARY	ENGLISH
plötzlich [*adv.*]	suddenly	leer [*adj.*]	empty
halb drei [*adv.*]	half past two	besonders [*adv.*]	especially
warum [*adv.*]	why	sein [*pron.*]	his
Ach so [*interj.*]	Oh yes; Oh, I see, ...	(der) Atem [*n.*]	breath, breathing
(die) Küche [*n.*]	kitchen	durch [*prep.*]	through
jemand [*pron.*]	somebody	dunkel [*adj.*]	dark, dim
gegen [*prep.*]	against	(die) Wohnung [*n.*]	apartment, flat
(der) Stuhl [*n.*]	chair	(die) Uhr [*n.*]	watch, clock
nach [*prep.*]	after	etwas [*pron.*]	something
still [*adj.*]	silent	weiß [*adj.*]	white
als [*conj.*]	when, as	(der) Küchenschrank [*n.*]	kitchen cabinet
(die) Hand [*n.*]	hand	(das) Licht [*n.*]	light
über [*prep.*]	over, across	(das) Hemd [*n.*]	shirt
(das) Bett [*n.*]	bed	nachts [*adv.*]	at night
neben [*prep.*]	next to, beside		

9.1 DIE KONSTRUKTION DES PRÄTERITUMS
CONSTRUCTING THE SIMPLE PAST

Being a 'simple' tense, the *Präteritum* is formed by adding certain endings to the main verb. As is the case with the *Präsens,* we need to drop the infinitive ending *-(e)n* in order to add the simple past endings to the verb stem. In doing so, we need to distinguish between regular and irregular verbs once again. Therefore, let us first have a look at the conjugation for regular verbs.

9.1.1 Regular Verbs

Regular verbs add the following endings to the stem in the *Präteritum*. We are using the regular verb *leben* again as an example:

	ENDING	EXAMPLE		ENGLISH	
1st **person** (sing.)	*-te*	*ich*	*lebte*	I	lived
2nd **person** (sing.)	*-test*	*du*	*lebtest*	you	lived
3rd **person** (sing.)	*-te*	*er/sie/es*	*lebte*	he/she/it	lived
1st **person** (pl.)	*-ten*	*wir*	*lebten*	we	lived
2nd **person** (pl.)	*-tet*	*ihr*	*lebtet*	you	lived
3rd **person** (pl.)	*-ten*	*sie*	*lebten*	they	lived
Formal (sing. & pl.)	*-ten*	*Sie*	*lebten*	you	lived

All weak (regular) verbs follow this predictable pattern, as exemplified in the following sentences from the short story at the beginning of this chapter:

> *Sie **überlegte**, warum sie aufgewacht war.*

> *Sie **horchte** nach der Küche.*

> *Sein Atem **fehlte**.*

Note that, just like in the present tense, **separable-prefix verbs** separate their prefix in main clauses of the simple past. This is true for both regular and irregular verbs with a separable prefix. The split-off prefix usually goes at the **end of the sentence**:

> *Plötzlich **wachte** sie **auf**.*   (→ infinitive verb: *aufwachen*, regular)

> *Sie **standen** sich im Hemd **gegenüber**.*   (→ infinitive verb: *gegenüberstehen,* irregular)

Variations:

- If the verb stem ends in **-d**, **-t**, or **-m** or **-n** following another consonant, then an additional **-e-** must be added before the **-te**, **-test**, or **-tet** endings (1st, 2nd, 3rd person singular and 2nd person plural). This is for reasons of easier pronunciation:

  landen (to land)   →   ich land**e**te, du land**e**test, ihr land**e**tet

  atmen (to breathe)   →   ich atm**e**te, du atm**e**test, ihr atm**e**tet

☞ DENK DARAN!

Overlooking the simple past signifier **-t-** embedded in the middle of these verbs can sometimes be a pitfall. It is especially important to pay close attention to the verb conjugations containing the endings **-te**, **-test**, **-ten**, and **-tet**. These endings indicate the simple past of a regular verb. However, do not forget that these suffixes may also signify the present tense conjugations of verbs whose stems have a **-t** ending. Here is a comparison:

Infinitive	Stem	Present Tense	Simple Past
starten (to start, to launch)	start-	ich start**e** wir start**en**	ich start**ete** wir start**eten**
beten (to pray)	bet-	du bet**est** sie bet**en**	du bet**etest** sie bet**eten**
warten (to wait)	wart-	ich wart**e** ihr wart**et**	ich wart**ete** ihr wart**etet**

9.1.2 Irregular Verbs

Most of the irregularities of strong verbs in the *Präteritum* are again caused by vowel changes. In this way, strong verbs may either change their stem vowel (*fahren → fuhr | geben → gab*) or their entire stem (*gehen → **ging***). Unfortunately, these vowel or stem changes are unpredictable and must be memorized. Personal endings are then added to the 'new' simple past stem. It is important to note, however, that the 1st and 3rd person singular do not take any simple past endings at all and only use the irregular verb stem.

	ENDING	fahren		geben		gehen	
1st **person** (sing.)	-	*ich*	*fuhr*	*ich*	*gab*	*ich*	*ging*
2nd **person** (sing.)	-st	*du*	*fuhrst*	*du*	*gabst*	*du*	*gingst*
3rd **person** (sing.)	-	*er/sie/ es*	*fuhr*	*er/sie/ es*	*gab*	*er/sie/ es*	*ging*
1st **person** (pl.)	-en	*wir*	*fuhren*	*wir*	*gaben*	*wir*	*gingen*
2nd **person** (pl.)	-t	*ihr*	*fuhrt*	*ihr*	*gabt*	*ihr*	*gingt*
3rd **person** (pl.)	-en	*sie*	*fuhren*	*sie*	*gaben*	*sie*	*gingen*
Formal (sing. & pl.)	-en	*Sie*	*fuhren*	*Sie*	*gaben*	*Sie*	*gingen*

Variations:

- If the stem of an irregular verb in the simple past ends in **-d**, **-s/ss/ß**, or **-t**, an additional **-e** is added to the **-st** ending (2nd person singular) and sometimes also to the **-t** ending (2nd person plural):

finden (to find)	→	fand	du fand**e**st	ihr fand**e**t
leiden (to suffer)	→	litt	du litt**e**st	ihr litt**e**t
lassen (to let)	→	ließ	du ließ**e**st	ihr ließt
reißen (to tear)	→	riss	du riss**e**st	ihr risst
reiten (to ride)	→	ritt	du ritt**e**st	ihr ritt**e**t

These variations, however, are very rarely used. In many cases, they are replaced with the respective conjugation in the **Perfekt** tense:

Littest du an einer Erkältung?   (Did you suffer from a cold?)
→ **Hast du** *an einer Erkältung* **gelitten***?*

Ließt ihr sie schlafen?   (Did you let her sleep?)
→ **Habt ihr** *sie schlafen* **gelassen***?*

9.1.3 Mixed Verbs

Just like in the *Perfekt* tense, there is a small group of **mixed verbs** that combine elements of regular and irregular verbs in the *Präteritum*. These verbs take the regular endings of weak verbs and at the same time undergo a vowel change. There are only about 20 verbs of this category, which tend to be frequently used. The most important ones are listed here:

VERB	ENGLISH		PRÄTERITUM
wissen	(to) know	→	*ich w**u**ss**te**, du w**u**ss**test**, er w**u**ss**te**, etc.*
denken	(to) think	→	*ich d**a**ch**te**, du d**a**ch**test**, er d**a**ch**te**, etc.*
brennen	(to) burn	→	*ich br**a**nn**te**, du br**a**nn**test**, er br**a**nn**te**, etc.*
bringen	(to) bring	→	*ich br**a**ch**te**, du br**a**ch**test**, er br**a**ch**te**, etc.*
rennen	(to) run	→	*ich r**a**nn**te**, du r**a**nn**test**, er r**a**nn**te**, etc.*
kennen	(to) know	→	*ich k**a**nn**te**, du k**a**nn**test**, er k**a**nn**te**, etc.*
nennen	(to) name	→	*ich n**a**nn**te**, du n**a**nn**test**, er n**a**nn**te**, etc.*

9.2 DAS PRÄTERITUM DER MODAL- UND HILFSVERBEN
THE SIMPLE PAST OF MODAL VERBS AND AUXILIARY VERBS

In terms of their behavior within the *Präteritum* (and also the *Perfekt*, though they are rarely used in that tense), **modal verbs** could be categorized as a subset of mixed verbs. The ones that have an *Umlaut* in the infinitive show a change to the respective vowel in the *Präteritum*. The remaining two modal verbs (*sollen* and *wollen*) behave exactly like regular verbs:

	dürfen	können	müssen	sollen	wollen	mögen
ich	durfte	konnte	musste	sollte	wollte	mochte
du	durftest	konntest	musstest	solltest	wolltest	mochtest
er/sie/es	durfte	konnte	musste	sollte	wollte	mochte
wir	durften	konnten	mussten	sollten	wollten	mochten
ihr	durftet	konntet	musstet	solltet	wolltet	mochtet
sie/Sie	durften	konnten	mussten	sollten	wollten	mochten

Just like in the present tense, modal verbs are the ones that are conjugated in the *Präteritum*, and the accompanying main verb remains in its infinitive form at the end of the sentence:

Conjugated modal (1st person singular, *Präteritum*)

*Ich **konnte** ihm nicht **helfen**.* ⟶ Main verb (in the infinitive)

***Wolltet** ihr gestern noch etwas **essen**?* ⟶ Main verb (in the infinitive)

Conjugated modal (2nd person plural, *Präteritum*)

The German **auxiliary verbs** all have irregular *Präteritum* forms and are conjugated as follows:

	haben	sein	werden
ich	hatte	war	wurde
du	hattest	warst	wurdest
er/sie/es	hatte	war	wurde
wir	hatten	waren	wurden
ihr	hattet	wart	wurdet
sie/Sie	hatten	waren	wurden

Note that any of these three verbs can only be used in the *Präteritum* if they are being used and conjugated as a main verb, without any other dependent verb. This is because the simple past functions as a 'simple' tense that does not require any auxiliary verbs:

Es **war** halb drei.
(It was half past two.)

(Not: Es war halb drei sein)

Damals **hatten** wir viele Freunde.
(We had many friends at the time.)

(Not: Damals hatten wir viele Freunde haben)

Ich **wurde** letztes Jahr Vater.
(I became a father last year.)

(Not: Ich wurde letztes Jahr Vater werden)

9.3 DER GEBRAUCH DES PRÄTERITUMS
THE USAGE OF THE SIMPLE PAST

The *Präteritum* is one of the three tenses that can be used to refer to the past in German. In strict grammatical terms, there is considerable overlap between the usage of the *Präteritum* and the *Perfekt* tense. This means that one tense can often be replaced with the other one in a grammatically correct way. In reality, however, and as we already mentioned in Chapter 8, the **Perfekt** tense is predominantly used in **conversation**, while the **Präteritum** is mostly employed in **writing**. This includes literary texts, stories, and novels, as well as scientific and formally written texts. Thus, the most important usage scenarios are as follows:

ⓘ GUT ZU WISSEN

Since the *Präteritum* is not very frequently used in spoken German, even native speakers sometimes have trouble applying the correct simple past forms. One example would be the verb *melken* (to milk), which is irregular and forms the simple past *molk* (*ich molk, du molkst, er molk,* etc.). However, many German native speakers use the regular form *melkte* instead, which has meanwhile become an acceptable variant that is also considered correct. Other such examples include:

backen (to bake) - *buk / backte*
saugen (to suck) - *sog / saugte*
wiegen (to weigh) - *wog / wiegte*
weben (to weave) - *wob / webte*

- **To talk about completed actions in the past**

  *Ich **war** sehr traurig, als meine Mutter letztes Jahr **starb**.*
  (I was very sad when my mother died last year.)

  *Die Arbeitslosigkeit **erreichte** 2009 ihren Höchststand.*
  (Unemployment reached its peak in 2009.)

  → Describes **past actions** that are completed without direct ties to the present. In this regard, the simple past is used in an identical way in both English and German. Frequent signal words include *letzte/n/s Woche/Monat/Jahr* (last week/month/year), *gestern* (yesterday), *vor langer Zeit* (a long time ago), *damals* (at that time).

- **To express past actions and events in literary and formal texts**

  *Hänsel und Gretel **saßen** um das Feuer, und als der Mittag **kam**, **aß** jeder sein Stücklein Brot.*
  (Hänsel and Gretel sat by the fire, and when noon came, each ate their little piece of bread.)

  → Literary text. Also used in the news, reports, and formal e-mails.

Exceptions

There are certain verbs that represent an exception to this guideline. The simple past forms of the **six modal verbs**, the verbs **sein**, **haben**, **werden**, and sometimes **wissen** are preferred over the perfect tense forms, both in spoken and written German.

ÜBUNGEN
EXERCISES

Ü 9.1) The following text is an adapted excerpt from the famous German fairy tale *Schneewittchen* (Snow White). Read the text and underline all verbs in the *Präteritum*. The first two have been done for you.

Nun <u>war</u> das arme Kind in dem großen Wald ganz allein. Da <u>hatte</u> es große Angst. Es wusste nicht, wo es war und fing an zu laufen, bis es bald Abend wurde. Da sah es ein kleines Häuschen und ging hinein. In dem Haus war alles klein: da stand ein Tisch mit sieben kleinen Tellern. Außerdem gab es sieben Messer und Gabeln und sieben Becher. An der Wand standen sieben Betten. Schneewittchen, weil es so hungrig und durstig war, aß von jedem Teller ein wenig Gemüse und Brot und trank aus jedem Becher einen Tropfen Wein. Dann, weil es so müde war, legte es sich in ein Bett, aber keins passte; das eine war zu lang, das andere zu kurz, bis endlich das siebente recht war: und darin blieb es liegen, dachte an den lieben Gott und schlief ein.

Ü 9.2) The following table gives you the infinitives of a number of verbs. Try to find the *Präteritum* forms for each of these verbs in the 1st person singular. If you feel stuck, you may consult the dictionary entry for the respective verb. In the third column, mark each verb as either a regular verb (=), an irregular verb (≠), or a mixed verb (+).

INFINITIVE	PRÄTERITUM (1ST PERSON SINGULAR)	TYPE	INFINITIVE	PRÄTERITUM (1ST PERSON SINGULAR)	TYPE
gehen			spielen		
fahren			sehen		
essen			nennen		
bleiben			schreiben		
arbeiten			nehmen		
machen			wohnen		
brennen			trinken		
kommen			treffen		
kaufen			stehen		
hören			sprechen		

Ü 9.3) The following sentences are all written in the *Perfekt* tense. Rewrite them using the *Präteritum.* One example has been given:

Example

Ich habe ein Steak gegessen.   →   Ich aß ein Steak.

a) Ich habe ein Buch gelesen.

_____

b) Du bist mit dem Bus zur Arbeit gefahren.

_____

c) Ich habe am Computer geschrieben.

_____

d) Habt ihr mit meiner Mutter gesprochen?

_____

e) Um sieben Uhr habe ich einen Freund getroffen.

_____

f) Um zwanzig Uhr sind wir ins Kino gegangen.

_____

g) Wir haben einen Film mit Tom Hanks gesehen.

_____

h) Danach haben wir noch etwas getrunken.

_____

i) Um ein Uhr ist er zu Hause gewesen.

_____

j) Haben Sie noch ein bisschen ferngesehen?

_____

Ü 9.4) Read through the following joke and fill in the gaps with the verbs in brackets. Each verb needs to be put into the correctly conjugated form in the *Präteritum*. You may use a dictionary for any unknown words but try to fill out as many gaps as possible on your own first.

Ein Lehrer, ein Politiker und ein Anwalt _____(sterben) und _____

(kommen) in den Himmel. St. Peter _____(sein) aber schlecht gelaunt, weil schon

so viele Menschen im Himmel _____(sein) und deshalb _____(wollen)

er es den dreien schwer machen. Als sie ans Tor _____(kommen), _____

(sagen) St. Peter zu ihnen, dass sie nur durch das Bestehen eines Tests in den Himmel kommen

_____(können): Alle drei _____(müssen) jeweils eine Frage beantworten.

St. Peter _____(wenden) sich also an den Lehrer und _____(sagen):

„Was _____(sein) der Name des Schiffes, das mit einem Eisberg _____

(kollidieren) und mit all seinen Passagieren _____(sinken)?" Der Lehrer

_____(denken) einen Moment nach und _____(antworten):

„Ich glaube, das _____(sein) die Titanic." St. Peter _____(lassen) ihn

durch das Tor. Er _____(hassen) aber Politiker und _____ (suchen) deshalb

nach einer schwierigeren Frage. St. Peter _____(wenden) sich an den Politiker

und _____(fragen): „Wie viele Menschen _____(sterben) auf dem

Schiff?" Der Politiker _____(haben) Glück, weil er ein Buch über die Titanic gelesen

hatte. Er _____(sagen): „1228". Das _____(sein) richtig und St. Peter

_____(lassen) ihn durch das Tor. Dann _____(wenden) sich St. Peter

an den Anwalt und _____(fragen): „Wie _____(heißen) die Opfer?"

KAPITEL 10 — DAS PLUSQUAMPERFEKT
CHAPTER 10 - THE PAST PERFECT

The past perfect tense, also referred to as pluperfect in English or **Plusquamperfekt** in German, is a compound tense that behaves very similarly in both English and German. It is used to talk about events that take place **before** another event in the *Präteritum* or *Perfekt* and emphasizes anteriority in the sequence of past events. This is also why this tense is sometimes called *Vorvergangenheit* ("past before the past") in German.

 Each of the following sentences exemplifies such a 'past-before-the-past' relationship:

Gestern bin ich mit Anna ausgegangen. *Ich **hatte** Anna lange nicht **gesehen**.*	Yesterday, I went out with Anna. I had not seen Anna for a long time.
*Letzte Woche war Peter in einen Autounfall verwickelt. Er **war** zehn Jahre lang unfallfrei **gefahren**.*	Peter was involved in a car accident last week. He had not had a car accident for ten years.
*Wir **hatten** das Essen **zubereitet**, bevor die Gäste kamen.*	We had been preparing the meal before the guests arrived.
*Nachdem die Gäste **gegessen hatten**, servierten wir Kaffee und Cognac.*	After the guests had eaten, we served coffee and brandy.

GERMAN VERB	ENGLISH	GERMAN VERB	ENGLISH
ausgehen (in etw.) verwickelt sein	(to) go out (to) be involved (in smth.)	zubereiten servieren	(to) prepare, (to) make (to) serve

GENERAL VOCABULARY	ENGLISH	GENERAL VOCABULARY	ENGLISH
(der) Autounfall [*n.*] zehn [*adv.*] unfallfrei [*adv.*] (das) Essen [*n.*]	car accident ten without accidents meal, food	bevor [*conj.*] (der) Gast [*n.*] nachdem [*conj.*] (der) Cognac [*n.*]	before guest after brandy

10.1 DIE KONSTRUKTION DES PLUSQUAMPERFEKTS
CONSTRUCTING THE PAST PERFECT

If you know the rules on how to form the German *Perfekt* tense, you already know most of what is required in the construction of the *Plusquamperfekt*. The only real difference is that the **auxiliary verb** is conjugated in the **simple past** instead of the simple present. The rules for forming the past participle, separable and inseparable prefixes, irregular past participles, and choosing between *sein* and *haben* as the auxiliary verb are the same that you would apply for the *Perfekt* tense.

10.1.1 Regular and Irregular Verbs

The *Plusquamperfekt* tense of most **regular** and **irregular** verbs is constructed by using the simple past tense of the auxiliary verb ***haben*** together with the **past participle** of the relevant main verb:

	AUXILIARY VERB (SIMPLE PAST)		PAST PARTICIPLE OF MAIN VERB
Ich	*hatte*	*Anna lange nicht*	*gesehen.*
Wir	*hatten*	*das Essen*	*zubereitet.*

Just like in the *Perfekt* tense, the past participle prefix ***ge-*** is added to the main verb, as well as the ending **-*t*** in the case of regular verbs, and **-*en*** for irregular verbs. **Separable prefix verbs** add the ge- in between their prefix and the stem, while **inseparable prefix verbs** do not take the ge- at all.

The rules regarding the **stem vowel changes** of irregular verbs in the past participle are exactly the same as with the *Perfekt* tense.

10.1.2 *Sein* as the auxiliary verb

As we already learned in chapter 8, main verbs that express **movement** or a **change in condition** require the auxiliary verb ***sein***. This rule also applies to the *Plusquamperfekt*. However, *sein* is conjugated in the **simple past**:

	AUXILIARY VERB (SIMPLE PAST)		PAST PARTICIPLE OF MAIN VERB
Er	*war*	*zehn Jahre lang unfallfrei*	*gefahren.*
Wir	*waren*	*schon nach Hause*	*gegangen.*

10.1.3 The Past Perfect in Main Clauses and Subordinate Clauses

When using the *Plusquamperfekt*, it is often the intention to emphasize a **sequence of events** in the past. This means, that a sentence may contain a **main clause** and a **subclause**, where one clause talks about a past event and the other clause references an action that took place even earlier.

Constructing these types of sentences has implications for the German word order, as we will briefly outline below.

As we already know, **main clauses** normally require the auxiliary verb to be in the second position, while the past participle goes at the end of the sentence.

In **subclauses**, however, the conjugated **auxiliary verb goes at the very end** of the sentence, even behind the past participle.

Examples:

	1	2	3	4
MAIN CLAUSE	*Ich*	***hatte***	*Anna lange nicht*	***gesehen***.
SUBCLAUSE	*Nachdem*	*die Gäste*	***gegessen***	***hatten,*** ...

As you can see, the example sentence for the main clause puts the auxiliary verb in the second position. Since it is a main clause, it is also a sentence that appears complete on its own. In the example featuring the subclause, the auxiliary verb comes after the past participle *gegessen*. This subclause cannot stand on its own and requires more information provided in the following main clause to be considered complete.

To connect a main clause and a subclause we often make use of **conjunctions**. A common conjunction used for sequencing events in the past is '***nachdem***' (after). It always appears in the part of the sentence that contains the *Plusquamperfekt* tense.

The subclause containing *nachdem* may appear before or after the main clause, but it is always separated from the main clause by a comma. In other words, it is up to you (and sometimes a matter of slightly different emphasis) whether you want to begin the sentence with the main clause or the subclause, as long as you separate the two using a comma. However, if the main clause appears after the subclause, then the regular 'subject-verb' word order of the main clause is inverted to 'verb-subject'.

Examples:

SUBCLAUSE	MAIN CLAUSE
Nachdem er geschlafen hatte, (After he had slept,	stand er auf. he got up.)
Nachdem ich Fußball gespielt hatte, (After playing football,	duschte ich mich. I took a shower.)
MAIN CLAUSE	**SUBCLAUSE**
Er stand auf, (He got up	nachdem er geschlafen hatte. after he had slept.)
Ich duschte mich, (I took a shower	nachdem ich Fußball gespielt hatte. after playing football.)

Another useful and frequently used conjunction for constructing sentences involving the *Plusquamperfekt* is '***bevor***' (before). It is usually used in subclauses containing the action that takes place later in the sequence of past events (i.e., the part of the sentence that features the *Präteritum* or *Perfekt*, and not the *Plusquamperfekt*).

Example:

SUBCLAUSE	MAIN CLAUSE
Bevor der Zug kam, (Before the train came,	hatte ich lange gewartet. I had been waiting for a long time.)
MAIN CLAUSE	**SUBCLAUSE**
Ich hatte lange gewartet, (I had been waiting for a long time	bevor der Zug kam. before the train came.)

10.2 DAS PLUSQUAMPERFEKT DER MODAL- UND HILFSVERBEN
THE PAST PERFECT OF MODAL VERBS AND AUXILIARY VERBS

The *Plusquamperfekt* of the German modal and auxiliary verbs is analogous to their formation in the *Perfekt* tense. The only difference is again the tense of the auxiliary verb, which needs to be conjugated in the **simple past**. The familiar past participles remain the same:

		dürfen	können	müssen	sollen	wollen	mögen	haben
ich	hatte							
du	hattest							
er/sie/es	hatte							
wir	hatten	*gedurft*	*gekonnt*	*gemusst*	*gesollt*	*gewollt*	*gemocht*	*gehabt*
ihr	hattet							
sie/Sie	hatten							

		sein	werden
ich	war		
du	warst		
er/sie/es	war		
wir	waren	*gewesen*	*geworden*
ihr	wart		
sie/Sie	waren		

10.3 DER GEBRAUCH DES PLUSQUAMPERFEKTS
THE USAGE OF THE PAST PERFECT

The *Plusquamperfekt* is a tense that is rarely used in isolation. As you have seen, it is usually employed when an action or event is described in the past and a more distant past needs to be expressed in relation to it. Accordingly, it is also one of the more rarely used tenses since such 'past-before-the-past' scenarios do not occur as frequently as other tenses. That said, however, German tends to be somewhat stricter than English with observing the correct sequence of past events when there is a clear scenario for it. Thus, bear the following guidelines in mind on how to use the *Plusquamperfekt*:

· **To show anteriority in relation to the *Präteritum* or *Perfekt***

   *Es ging ihm schlecht, weil er zu viel **gegessen hatte**.*
   (He was feeling sick because he had eaten too much.)

   *Nachdem ich das Auto **vollgetankt hatte**, fuhren wir los.*
   (After I had filled up the car we set off.)

   → Describes **past events** that took place **before** another event in the past. Common signal words indicating such a sequence of events include *nachdem* (after), *bevor* (before), *als* (when), and *schon* (already).

❶ GUT ZU WISSEN

The *Plusquamperfekt* is one of those tenses that receive a bit of a sloppy treatment, even (or especially) by native speakers. While considerable flexibility is possible regarding the use of the *Präteritum* and *Perfekt*, the *Plusquamperfekt* should be employed correctly within the appropriate sequence of past events. In reality, however, many native speakers use the perfect or simple past instead. This is grammatically incorrect, but still very common.

Correct: *„Er hat fantastisch Klavier gespielt, weil er vorher viel geübt hatte.“*

Common (but wrong): *„Er hat fantastisch Klavier gespielt, weil er vorher viel geübt hat.“*

Therefore, do not worry too much if you are having difficulty applying the *Plusquamperfekt* correctly. Chances are you will still get your point across. However, do make it your goal to keep practicing your understanding and correct usage of all the different tenses.

Ü 10.1) Complete the following sentences using the Plusquamperfekt. Be mindful of irregular verbs and choose correctly between *sein* and *haben* as the auxiliary verbs.

a) Nachdem er nach München _____(fahren), war er sehr müde.

b) Letztes Jahr zogen wir in die Stadt, in der meine Großeltern _____(leben).

c) Er _____fünf Bier _____(trinken), als er nach Hause ging.

d) Als mein Chef mich anrief, _____ich schon nach Hause _____(gehen).

e) Nachdem das Wetter so schlecht _____(werden), mussten wir die Feier absagen.

Ü 10.2) Bring all the following actions into a sequence of past events using the Plusquamperfekt and the conjunction *nachdem*. Form one complete sentence for each action pair. The first three actions have been given as an example.

Example:

aufstehen / Frühstück machen / zur Arbeit fahren

→ 1) Nachdem ich aufgestanden war, machte ich Frühstück.

2) Nachdem ich Frühstück gemacht hatte, fuhr ich zur Arbeit.

a) zur Arbeit fahren / mit dem Chef sprechen

_____

b) mit dem Chef sprechen / zu Mittag essen

_____

c) zu Mittag essen / Kunden anrufen

_____

d) Kunden anrufen / nach Hause gehen

_____

e) nach Hause gehen / fernsehen

_____

f) fernsehen / einschlafen

_____

Ü 10.3) Decide which of the three past tenses has been used in the following sentences. Sometimes a sentence is divided into main clause and subclause, each with a different tense. Use the abbreviations Pr (Präteritum), Pf (Perfekt), and Ppf (Plusquamperfekt).

a) Gestern ging ich mit meiner Freundin auf eine Party.

_____

b) Bevor wir das Haus verließen, hatten wir noch zu Abend gegessen.

_____

c) Nachdem uns das Taxi zur Party gebracht hatte, haben wir unsere Freunde begrüßt.

_____

d) Wir hatten viel Spaß und blieben bis zwei Uhr nachts.

_____

KAPITEL 11 — DAS FUTUR I
CHAPTER 11 - THE SIMPLE FUTURE

The simple future, or *Futur I* in German, is a **compound tense** that is far less frequently used than its English counterpart. It is, however, an important tense to be familiar with since it can be employed to express **assumptions** and **probabilities**, along with events taking place in the future.

 One of the advantages of this tense is its straightforward and predictable formation. Once you are familiar with the pattern, you will be able to conjugate all German verbs in the future, regular and irregular alike. Have a look at the following example sentences:

*Ich **werde** in meinem neuen Job mehr Verantwortung übernehmen **müssen**.*	I will have to take on more responsibility in my new job.
*Das Klima **wird** sich immer mehr **verändern**.*	The climate will increasingly change.
*Wir **werden** für dich ein Stück Kuchen **aufheben**.*	We will save a piece of cake for you.
*Er **wird** bestimmt müde **sein**, wenn er ankommt.*	He will surely be tired when he arrives.
*Ihr Zimmer **wird** wohl immer noch so chaotisch **aussehen**.*	Her room will probably still look just as messy.

GERMAN VERB	ENGLISH	GERMAN VERB	ENGLISH
übernehmen	(to) take on, (to) assume	aufheben	(to) save; (to) pick up
(sich) verändern	(to) change	aussehen	(to) look, (to) appear

GENERAL VOCABULARY	ENGLISH	GENERAL VOCABULARY	ENGLISH
neu [*adj.*]	new	(der) Kuchen [*n.*]	cake
(der) Job [*n.*]	job	bestimmt [*adv.*]	certainly, surely
mehr [*adv.*]	more	ihr [*pron.*]	her
(die) Verantwortung [*n.*]	responsibility	(das) Zimmer [*n.*]	room
(das) Klima [*n.*]	climate	wohl [*adv.*]	probably
immer mehr [*adv.*]	increasingly (more)	immer noch [*adv.*]	still
für dich [*prep.*] [*pron.*]	for you	so [*adv.*]	so
(das) Stück [*n.*]	piece	chaotisch [*adj.*]	chaotic, messy

11.1 DIE KONSTRUKTION DES FUTUR I
CONSTRUCTING THE SIMPLE FUTURE

Constructing the *Futur I* tense follows the same pattern as the English "will-future" construction, where the auxiliary verb 'will' (or 'shall') is joined up with the main verb in the infinitive:

| I | **will** | **return** | the library books tomorrow. |
| I | **will** | **take** | my umbrella because it might rain. |

future auxiliary   main verb in the infinitive

In German, we use the auxiliary verb **werden** and the **infinitive of the main verb**. The verb *werden* needs to be conjugated in the present tense to agree with the subject, and the infinitive remains unchanged. This is true for regular and irregular main verbs alike. The conjugated auxiliary verb usually goes in the 2nd position of the sentence, while the infinitive is placed at the end:

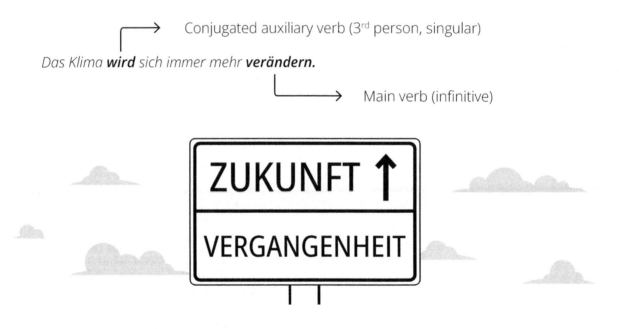

Conjugated auxiliary verb (3rd person, singular)

Das Klima **wird** *sich immer mehr* **verändern.**

Main verb (infinitive)

As you know from Chapter 6.3, the word order is different in questions, where the subject and the conjugated part of the predicate (i.e., *werden* in this case) are reversed:

Wird sich das Klima *immer mehr verändern?*

Warum **wird sich das Klima** *immer mehr verändern?*

Based on the number and person of the subject, the auxiliary verb *werden* needs to be conjugated in the present tense, as shown in Chapter 7.1.4. Here is that conjugation table for better continuity:

	werden		MAIN VERB IN THE INFINITIVE
1st person (sing.)	*ich*	**werde**	
2nd person (sing.)	*du*	**wirst**	
3rd person (sing.)	*er/sie/es*	**wird**	*machen, kommen, denken, kennen, aufstehen, fahren, sagen, einkaufen, überlegen...etc.*
1st person (pl.)	*wir*	**werden**	
2nd person (pl.)	*ihr*	**werdet**	
3rd person (pl.)	*sie/Sie*	**werden**	

11.2 DAS FUTUR I MIT MODALVERBEN
THE SIMPLE FUTURE WITH MODAL VERBS

Forming the *Futur I* tense of modal verbs is very straightforward and follows the same pattern we outlined above. Thus, if a modal verb appears on its own in a sentence like "I will want ice cream", it can be translated as "*Ich werde ein Eis wollen*" in German. However, let us remember that modal verbs are usually used in conjunction with a main verb which they modify.

Therefore, the future tense of modal verbs is constructed with the finite form of **werden** + **the infinitive of the main verb** + **the infinitive of the modal**:

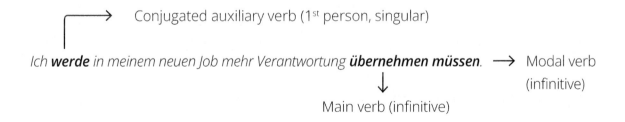

Note that the infinitive of the modal verb goes after the infinitive of the main verb and that both are positioned at the end of the sentence.

11.3 DAS PRÄSENS ALS FUTUR
USING THE PRESENT TENSE TO EXPRESS THE FUTURE

Although it is true that the *Futur I* tense can be used to talk about future events, let us have a closer look at the fact that the **present tense** is often preferred when referring to the future, especially in spoken German. We already mentioned this in chapter 7.2, but we would like to give you some more context. Compare the following two sentences:

Ich werde nach Norwegen fahren.
Ich fahre nächste Woche nach Norwegen.

Both the above sentences establish the fact that the speaker will travel to Norway in the future. The first sentence achieves this by employing the *Futur I*, while the second sentence uses the *Präsens* and a specific **time indication** (*"nächste Woche"*). In the first sentence it is not clear 'when' the journey will take place, only that it will take place in the future. The second sentence gives us a more precise future point in time. Now, have a look at the following sentence:

Ich fahre nach Norwegen.

In this sentence the speaker only tells us about their journey to Norway. Whether they are travelling there now, on a regular basis, or if they will travel to Norway in the future remains ambiguous, though the sentence could describe each of these scenarios from a grammatical point of view.

The above examples aim to illustrate that a **time indication** or an **obvious future context is needed** if the *Präsens* is used to describe a future event. Common time expressions for the future include *morgen* (tomorrow), *nächste/n/s Woche/Monat/Jahr* (next week/month/year), *bald* (soon), *später* (later), *am Sonntag / Montag etc.* (on Sunday / Monday etc.).

However, if the time of the future action is not clear or unknown, the *Futur I* needs to be used:

Ich werde weniger essen.   (*I am going to eat less.*)
Was wirst du tun?   (*What will you do?*)

11.4 DER GEBRAUCH DES FUTUR I
THE USAGE OF THE SIMPLE FUTURE

Although the *Präsens* is frequently used to express future actions (especially plans), the *Futur I* still has distinct usage scenarios, which are as follows:

- **To indicate a future intention**

  *Wir **werden** für dich ein Stück Kuchen **aufheben**.*

  → Describes intention. The use of the *Futur I* often adds a sense of determination or emphasis to the expressed intention.

- **To express an assumption about the future**

  *Er **wird** bestimmt müde **sein**, wenn er ankommt.*

  → It is assumed that he will be tired. Common signal words that often accompany such assumptions include *bestimmt* (surely), *sicherlich* (certainly), and *mit Sicherheit* (with certainty).

- **To express an assumption or probability about the present**

  *Ihr Zimmer **wird** wohl immer noch so chaotisch **aussehen**.*

  → It is probable that her room will still be messy. Signal words such as *wohl, wahrscheinlich,* or *vermutlich* (all of them meaning 'probably' or 'presumably') help emphasize the sense of strong probability in such statements.

ÜBUNGEN
EXERCISES

Ü 11.1) The following statements talk about the future by using the Präsens + a time indicator. Rephrase each sentence using the *Futur I* to give it an increased sense of determination. One example has been given.

Example: Ich gehe morgen ins Büro.   →   Ich werde morgen ins Büro gehen.

a) Er kauft nächsten Monat ein Auto.

_____

b) Gehst du heute Abend auf die Party?

_____

c) Ihr müsst morgen zur Arbeit gehen.

_____

d) Gehst du nächstes Jahr in Rente?

_____

e) Wir sprechen später mit dem Chef.

_____

Ü 11.2) Use the following clues to make assumptions about the activities or states of different people. Use a fitting signal word to mark it is an assumption. One example has been given.

Example: sie / Brot backen   →   Sie wird wahrscheinlich Brot backen.

a) Peter / traurig sein

_____

b) Ich / mit dem Zug fahren

_____

c) Es / nicht lange dauern

_____

d) Wir / ein Auto kaufen

_____

e) Ihr / mehr Verantwortung übernehmen

_____

Ü 11.3) Form complete sentences using the future tense with _werden_ and say what these people will do on the weekend.

Example: ich → einkaufen gehen   →   Ich werde am Wochenende einkaufen gehen.

a) Helmut → ein Buch lesen

_____

b) Jörg → in ein Restaurant gehen

_____

c) Karin und Anna → zu Hause bleiben

_____

d) ich → Freunde besuchen

_____

e) du → viel fernsehen

_____

f) die Müllers → eine Party feiern

_____

g) Katja → im Büro arbeiten

_____

h) Opa → einen Film sehen

_____

KAPITEL 12 — DAS FUTUR II
CHAPTER 12 - THE FUTURE PERFECT

The *Futur II*, or future perfect in English, is one of the two tenses that can be used to express future actions and events in German. It is somewhat of an unusual tense and therefore not used very often. Its formation and function bear many similarities to its English counterpart and, given your knowledge of all the other German tenses, it should not pose too many difficulties for you.

 Have a look at the following dialogue, in which newlyweds Dirk and Lea discuss what they will have experienced and achieved 30 years from now:

Dirk:	*In 30 Jahren werden wir ein Haus gebaut haben. Was glaubst du, Schatz?*	Dirk:	In 30 years, we will have built a house. What do you think, darling?
Lea:	*Das nehme ich an! Und wir werden mindestens zwei Kinder großgezogen haben.*	Lea:	I suppose so! And we will have raised at least two children.
Dirk:	*Vielleicht werden unsere Kinder bereits Kinder bekommen haben!*	Dirk:	Maybe our children will already have had children!
Lea:	*Das kann schon sein. Werden wir auch viel gereist sein?*	Lea:	Quite possibly. Will we also have travelled a lot?
Dirk:	*Eher nicht. Das Leben wird für uns gerade erst etwas ruhiger geworden sein.*	Dirk:	Probably not. Life will only just have become a bit quieter for us.

GERMAN VERB	ENGLISH	GERMAN VERB	ENGLISH
bauen glauben	(to) build (to) believe, (to) think	annehmen großziehen	(to) assume, (to) suppose (to) raise

GENERAL VOCABULARY	ENGLISH	GENERAL VOCABULARY	ENGLISH
(der) Schatz [n.] mindestens [adv.] zwei [adv.] vielleicht [adv.] unser / -e [pron.] bereits [adv.] schon [part.]	darling (lit. treasure) at least two maybe, perhaps our already particle for emphasis	eher nicht [adv.] (das) Leben [n.] für uns [prep.] [pron.] gerade erst [adv.] etwas [adv.] ruhig [adj.]	rather not, not really life for us just recently somewhat, a bit quiet

12.1 DIE KONSTRUKTION DES FUTUR II
CONSTRUCTING THE FUTURE PERFECT

The *Futur II* tense combines elements of the simple future and the *Perfekt* tense. This makes sense if we consider the fact that the *Futur II* expresses **anteriority** in relation to the simple future. In other words, events taking place in the *Futur II* will have happened in the future and are being looked back on from the perspective of the *Futur I*. In order to form the future perfect, we need 3 elements:

werden (conjugated, in 2nd position) + **past participle** (main verb) + **haben / sein** (infinitive, at the end)

	werden		PAST PARTICIPLE OF MAIN VERB	haben / sein
1st person (sing.) **2nd person** (sing.) **3rd person** (sing.)	*ich* *du* *er/sie/es*	*werde* *wirst* *wird*	*gemacht, gedacht, gekannt, gesagt, eingekauft, überlegt...etc.*	*haben*
1st person (pl.) **2nd person** (pl.) **3rd person** (pl.)	*wir* *ihr* *sie/Sie*	*werden* *werdet* *werden*	*gekommen, gelaufen, aufgestanden, gefahren, gestorben...etc*	*sein*

Note that all the rules regarding the formation of the **past participle** as discussed in previous chapters hold true here. This includes the rules on regular and irregular endings, vowel changes in irregular and mixed verbs, and the position of the past participle *ge-* in verbs with separable and inseparable prefixes.

Similarly, choosing between *haben* and *sein* as the **auxiliary verb** follows all the familiar guidelines as you know them from previous chapters. At this point, the only real new information required to form the *Futur II* is the order in which all these elements appear within a sentence. Let us have a look at a few more examples from the dialogue section of this chapter:

	werden (CONJUGATED, PRESENT TENSE)		PAST PARTICIPLE OF MAIN VERB	AUXILIARY VERB (INFINITIVE)
In 30 Jahren	**werden**	*wir ein Haus*	**gebaut**	**haben.**
Vielleicht	**werden**	*unsere Kinder bereits Kinder*	**bekommen**	**haben.**
Das Leben	**wird**	*für uns gerade erst etwas ruhiger*	**geworden**	**sein.**

Likewise, the word order rules for **questions** in the Futur II are the same ones that you are familiar with for other tenses. The conjugated part of the **predicate** (i.e., the conjugated form of *werden*) swaps position with the **subject** of the sentence in 'yes-or-no-questions':

1	2	...	END OF SENTENCE	
werden (CONJUGATED, PRESENT TENSE)	SUBJECT		PAST PARTICIPLE OF MAIN VERB	AUXILIARY VERB (INFINITIVE)
Werden	*wir*	*auch viel*	*gereist*	*sein?*

However, if a **question word** is involved, then the question word takes the first position, while the other parts of the sentence are added on in the same order as they would appear in a 'yes-or-no-question':

1	2		...	END OF SENTENCE	
QUESTION WORD	werden (CONJUGATED, PRESENT TENSE)	SUBJECT		PAST PARTICIPLE OF MAIN VERB	AUXILIARY VERB (INFINITIVE)
Wann	*wirst*	*du*	*ein Haus*	*gebaut*	*haben?*

12.2 DER GEBRAUCH DES FUTUR II
THE USAGE OF THE FUTURE PERFECT

The *Futur II* is not a tense you will use very often. Especially as a beginning leaner of German it is more important to be aware of its existence and to be able to understand it when you hear a native speaker use it. As you get more exposure to the language and become more comfortable with the different tenses and their usage, you will naturally start expressing yourself with greater nuance, which will include the use of the *Futur II*. With that said, the *Futur II* is primarily used to express the following things:

- **For assumptions, hopes or plans that an action will be completed in the future**

  *Morgen **wird** er das Auto hoffentlich **repariert haben**.*
  (Hopefully, he will have fixed the car by tomorrow.)

  *Wenn ich aus dem Urlaub zurückkomme, **werde** ich viel **erlebt haben**.*
  (When I return from my vacation, I will have experienced a lot.)

  → Describes a future point in time by which something will have been completed. When using the *Futur II* in this way, it is important to use a **time expression** that indicates the time by which the action will be completed, unless that point in time is obvious from the context of what is being said. Time indications that are commonly used in these instances include *bis dahin* (by then), *bereits* (already), *bis zum Montag / 31. Januar etc.* (by Monday / January 31st etc.).

- **For assumptions about an action in the past**

  *Peter ist nicht hier. Er **wird** wohl den Zug **verpasst haben**.*
  (Peter is not here. He probably missed the train.)

  *Susanne sieht traurig aus. Sie **wird** wahrscheinlich Streit mit ihrem Mann **gehabt haben**.*
  (Susanne looks sad. She probably had an argument with her husband.)

  → Expresses a (probable) assumption about what happened in the past. Common signal words associated with this usage include *wohl* (likely), *wahrscheinlich* (probably), and *bestimmt* (certainly).

ℹ GUT ZU WISSEN

The *Futur II* is rarely used in contemporary German. In many instances, you will hear native speakers use the *Perfekt* tense instead, especially in spoken German:

Wenn er ankommt, werde ich bereits abgereist sein.
(I will have departed when he arrives.)

→ *Wenn er ankommt, **bin** ich bereits **abgereist**.*

ÜBUNGEN
EXERCISES

Ü 12.1) All the following sentences are written in the *Futur II* tense. Decide which auxiliary verb needs to go at the end.

a) Sie wird schon nach Hause gegangen _____.

b) Bis dahin werden wir mindestens noch einmal einkaufen gegangen _____.

c) In zehn Jahren werde ich in Rente gegangen _____.

d) Wenn ihr zurückkommt, werde ich schon das Essen für euch gekocht _____.

e) In spätestens einer Stunde wird das Kind eingeschlafen _____.

Ü 12.2) Form complete sentences in the *Futur II* using the clues given. Be aware that some of the sentences are questions. One example has been done for you.

Example:

er / gehen / schon / nach Hause   →   Er wird schon nach Hause gegangen sein.

a) Bis dahin / ich / schon wieder / aufwachen

_____

b) Warum / du / bis morgen / deine Arbeit / erledigen?

_____

c) Nächstes Jahr / wir / zum ersten Mal / in den Urlaub fahren

_____

d) Er / das / wohl / wissen

_____

e) Deine Eltern / bis sieben Uhr / kochen?

_____

Ü 12.3) Imagine you are writing a dystopian science-fiction novel in which the following things will have happened by the year 2300. Write complete sentences in the *Futur II:*

a) Außerirdische landen auf der Erde

_____

b) Das Klima wird wärmer

_____

c) Computer übernehmen die Weltherrschaft

_____

d) Das Polareis schmilzt

_____

e) Die Kontinente versinken im Meer

_____

f) 90% der Menschen sterben

_____

Unit 3

VERB VOICE
& VERB MOOD

Having acquired an in-depth understanding of the different German tenses, their formation, and usage in Unit 2, this last Unit will examine a number of additional verb properties and behaviors. Thus, we will learn how to utilize the so-called **voice** of a verb to change perspective between subject and object and the associated importance of any given **action being carried out**. A closer look at the different **moods** of a verb will help us express commands through the use of the **imperative**. It will also acquaint us with both the *Konjunktiv I* and *Konjunktiv II*, each of which serving a different function. Thus, we will be able to express wishes, directives, and possibilities with more nuance. It will also enable us to turn direct speech into indirect speech.

KAPITEL 13 — DAS PASSIV
CHAPTER 13 - THE PASSIVE VOICE

As we already know from the first chapter in Unit 1, sentences can be constructed in two different ways to make either the subject or the object the focal point of the sentence. We refer to it as an **active** sentence if the **subject** is the focus and the entity carrying out the action. A **passive** sentence, on the other hand, puts the emphasis on the **object** receiving the action, while the subject is not as important or perhaps even unknown. Verbs are crucial in constructing sentences in either one of these ways and we call these two perspectives the **voice of the verb**.

 Study and listen to the following sentences, which all contain the passive voice:

Das Haus **wird gebaut**.	The house is being built.
Das Haus **wird von Peter gebaut**.	The house is being built by Peter.
Das Fenster **wird** *langsam* **geöffnet**.	The window is slowly being opened.
Das Fenster **ist** *seit einiger Zeit* **geöffnet**.	The window has been open for some time.
Das Buch **wird geschrieben**.	The book is being written.
Heute **sind** *die* Läden **geschlossen**.	The shops are closed today.
Es **wurde** *viel* **getrunken** *auf der Party*.	People drank a lot at the party.

GERMAN VERB	ENGLISH	GERMAN VERB	ENGLISH
bauen	(to) build	schreiben	(to) write
öffnen	(to) open	schließen	(to) close

GENERAL VOCABULARY	ENGLISH	GENERAL VOCABULARY	ENGLISH
(das) Haus [*n.*] (das) Fenster [*n.*] langsam [*adv.*]	house window slowly	seit einiger Zeit [*adv. Dat.*] (der) Laden [*n.*]	for some time shop, store

13.1 AKTIV - UND PASSIVSÄTZE
ACTIVE AND PASSIVE SENTENCES

Peter baut das Haus.

This is an **active** sentence because there is somebody (the **subject**) carrying out the action, in this case Peter. He is the one doing the building and the house is the one receiving the action (i.e., the **object**).

If we now want to look at the action from the perspective of the object, we may shift the focus towards the house and say:

*Das Haus **wird gebaut**.*

This is a **passive** sentence, and the house is the center of attention, along with the action it receives. The house has changed roles from being the object to being the subject of the sentence. This means the **subject** is now the **receiver** of the action expressed through the verb in the passive voice. Furthermore, the sentence does not even mention Peter and it could really be anybody doing the building.

However, if we want to keep Peter in the picture as the builder, we may add this bit of information using the prepositions *von* or *durch*. Thus, we can say:

*Das Haus **wird von Peter gebaut**.*

Now we have included Peter as the so-called **agent**, thereby retaining every piece of information from the original active sentence.

13.2 DAS VORGANGSPASSIV UND DAS ZUSTANDSPASSIV
THE PROCESS PASSIVE AND THE STATUS PASSIVE

There are two types of passive voice in German: the **process passive** and the **status passive**, each describing a different kind of action.

The **process passive** emphasizes that an action is being carried out onto somebody or something:

> *Das Fenster **wird** langsam **geöffnet**.*
> → The window is in the process of being opened.

The **status passive**, however, highlights the state or condition that somebody or something is in:

> *Das Fenster **ist** seit einiger Zeit **geöffnet**.*
> → The window has been open for some time.

In the following sections we will examine the different meanings, constructions, and uses of each of these types of passives in more detail.

13.2.1 The Process Passive

We use the **process passive** if we want to emphasize the **action of a sentence** (i.e. 'what' happened) and who received the action. Who carried out the action is not as important or may not even be known. The present tense of this type of passive voice is formed using the auxiliary verb ***werden*** (conjugated in the appropriate tense) + the **past participle of the main verb**:

Conjugated form of *werden* (3rd person, sing., *Präsens*)

*Das Buch **wird geschrieben**.* ⟶ Past participle of main verb (*schreiben*)

As mentioned earlier, the agent can (but need not be) mentioned by adding *von / durch [...]* after the conjugated part of the predicate:

> *Das Buch wird **von Peter** geschrieben.*

The process passive can appear in all six tenses. The following table lists the active sentence in the relevant tense (for our purposes we will let Peter carry out the action again), along with the "formula" for the passive, and finally the passive sentence in the relevant tense. Note that you will not encounter the passive voice in the *Plusquamperfekt* or *Futur II* very often. We are still including them here for completeness:

TENSE	ACTIVE	PASSIVE FORMULA	PASSIVE
Präsens	Peter schreibt das Buch.	simple present of *werden* + past participle	*Das Buch* **wird** *(von Peter)* **geschrieben.**
Perfekt	Peter hat das Buch geschrieben.	simple present of *sein* + past participle + *'worden'*	*Das Buch* **ist** *(von Peter)* **geschrieben worden.**
Präteritum	Peter schrieb das Buch.	simple past of *werden* + past participle	*Das Buch* **wurde** *(von Peter)* **geschrieben.**
Plusquamperfekt	Peter hatte das Buch geschrieben.	simple past of *sein* + past participle + *'worden'*	*Das Buch* **war** *(von Peter)* **geschrieben worden.**
Futur I	Peter wird das Buch schreiben.	simple present of *werden* + past participle + *'werden'*	*Das Buch* **wird** *(von Peter)* **geschrieben werden.**
Futur II	Peter wird das Buch geschrieben haben.	simple present of *werden* + past participle + *'worden'* + *'sein'*	*Das Buch* **wird** *(von Peter)* **geschrieben worden sein.**

As you can see, the *Perfekt*, the *Plusquamperfekt*, and the *Futur II* constructions contain the word "*worden*". It may look a bit confusing at first, but this is the **past participle form of the auxiliary verb *werden*** (not of the main verb *werden*), which is our passive voice signifier. *Werden*, the auxiliary verb, and *werden*, the main verb, have identical conjugations, except for the past participle.

13.2.2 The Status Passive

The **status passive** describes the **result** of an action that has been done to somebody or something. It expresses the 'status' that the person or thing now has, after the action has been completed. Compare the following two sentences:

Die Läden wurden von den Ladenbesitzern geschlossen.
(The shops were closed by the shop owners.)

Heute sind die Läden geschlossen.
(The shops are closed today.)

The first sentence uses the process passive as explained in the previous section. We are told that the action of 'closing' was performed on the shops. In the second sentence, however, we see the result of that action: The shops now have a 'closed' status, as it were. It is not important who closed them, only that they are not open today.

The present tense of the status passive is formed with a conjugated form of **sein** + **past participle**:

Conjugated form of *sein* (3rd person, plural, *Präsens*)

Heute sind die Läden geschlossen. ⟶ Past participle of main verb (*schließen*)

Just like the process passive, the status passive can appear in all six tenses:

TENSE	PASSIVE FORMULA	PASSIVE
Präsens	simple present of *sein* + past participle	*Die Läden* **sind geschlossen**.
Perfekt	simple present of *sein* + past participle + past participle of *sein*	*Die Läden* **sind geschlossen gewesen**.
Präteritum	simple past of *sein* + past participle	*Die Läden* **waren geschlossen**.
Plusquamperfekt	simple past of *sein* + past participle + past participle of *sein*	*Die Läden* **waren geschlossen gewesen**.
Futur I	simple present of *werden* + past participle + 'sein'	*Die Läden* **werden geschlossen sein**.
Futur II	simple present of *werden* + past participle + past participle of *sein* + 'sein'	*Die Läden* **werden geschlossen gewesen sein**.

13.3 DAS UNPERSÖNLICHE PASSIV
THE IMPERSONAL PASSIVE

In English, only transitive verbs can be used in the passive voice. In essence, a **transitive verb** is a verb that is usually accompanied by a direct object (i.e., an object in the accusative case). For example, the sentence "Peter is buying a dog" contains the transitive verb 'to buy', while 'a dog' would be the direct object of the purchase. Consequently, this sentence could be rendered in the passive voice as "A dog was bought by Peter". **Intransitive verbs**, on the other hand, **do not take a direct object**. For instance, a sentence like "We walked to the station" uses the intransitive verb 'to walk'. In English, there is no way to render this sentence in the passive voice as something like "To the station was walked", since this would not make any sense.

In German, however, we can sometimes use intransitive verbs in the passive voice. Such constructions are called **impersonal passives** since the verb expresses an activity without requiring a personal subject carrying out the action. The emphasis is on the activity, rather than on who is doing it. In place of a personal subject, the impersonal pronoun **es** is introduced as a placeholder (also known as an 'impersonal subject'). The auxiliary verb *werden* is conjugated to agree with *es*.

ACTIVE	Die Gäste haben auf der Party viel getrunken. (The guests drank a lot at the party.)
PASSIVE	Es wurde viel getrunken auf der Party. (People drank a lot at the party. Lit.: 'It was drunk a lot at the party')

Note that *es* is merely a placeholder and plays no grammatical role in such a construction. If any other element is moved to the first position, the *es* disappears:

Auf der Party wurde viel getrunken.

A common way of maintaining this impersonal nature in an active sentence is the use of the pronoun *man*. It is very similar to *es* in its function of replacing the personal subject in a sentence, but is usually only employed in active sentences:

Man trank viel auf der Party.

☞ DENK DARAN!

German sentences usually sound better if they are written in the active voice. Sentences in the passive sometimes sound long-winded and unnatural. There are different ways to avoid a passive construction:

„Dieses Auto wird häufig gekauft."

Viele Leute kaufen dieses Auto. /
Dieses Auto ist sehr beliebt. /
Dieses Auto ist ein Verkaufsschlager.

ÜBUNGEN
EXERCISES

Ü 13.1) Complete the following sentences in the passive voice with the appropriate form of *werden* in the *Präsens*.

a) Du _____ hier noch gebraucht.

b) Ich _____ jeden Morgen von meiner Frau geweckt.

c) Die Tower Bridge _____ von Touristen oft besucht.

d) Wir _____ von deinen Eltern zu ihrer Geburtstagsparty eingeladen.

e) Das Abendessen _____ ab sechs Uhr serviert.

f) Die Patienten _____ mit den neuesten Methoden behandelt.

g) _____ ihr von seinen Schwiegereltern abgeholt?

h) Die Handys _____ im Ausland produziert.

Ü 13.2) Re-write the following passive sentences in the active voice. One example has been provided.

Example:

Das Zimmer ist von euch aufgeräumt worden. → Ihr habt das Zimmer aufgeräumt.

a) Der Hund ist von uns gefüttert worden.

_____

b) Die Teller sind von dir gewaschen worden.

_____

c) Das Flugzeug wird vom Piloten gelandet.

_____

d) Ihr werdet von mir gerufen.

_____

e) Das Kind wurde von der Mutter gebadet.

_____

f) Das Kind wird vom Vater gelobt werden.

_____

Ü 13.3) Re-write the following active sentences in the passive voice. We have provided one example.

Example:
Der Hund hat Peter gebissen.   →   Peter wurde von dem Hund gebissen.

a) Klaus füttert die Katze.

_____

b) Klaus wird den Computer benutzen.

_____

c) Inge hatte ein Buch geschrieben.

_____

d) Der Lehrer erklärte den Schülern das Problem.

_____

e) Der Vater fährt den Jungen zum Fußballtraining.

_____

f) Ich werde den Kunden anrufen.

_____

Ü 13.4) Form sentences in the impersonal passive. Remember that there is no subject in these sentences. Use the placeholder 'es' instead. One example has been provided.

Example:

Man arbeitet den ganzen Tag.   →   Es wird den ganzen Tag gearbeitet

a) Morgens liest man beim Frühstück die Zeitung.

_____

b) Man spricht immer leise.

_____

c) Am Wochenende spielt man.

_____

d) Abends geht man mit Freunden aus.

_____

e) Nachts schläft man in warmen Betten.

_____

KAPITEL 14 — DER IMPERATIV
CHAPTER 14 - THE IMPERATIVE

Verbs can assume different **moods**. These moods express the speaker's **attitude** toward what is being said (i.e., a statement of fact, a wish, a command, etc.). The **imperative** is a verb mood that is used to formulate requests and commands. Both English and German can form the imperative, though German distinguishes between singular and plural imperative forms, as well as formal and informal addresses. Apart from the **three** German imperative forms, this chapter also takes into consideration two constructions that express commands, although they are not imperatives grammatically. They are, however, related to the imperative semantically.

 The following sentences present you with different sets of imperative sentences, each focusing on a particular imperative form:

***Besuch** mich mal wieder!*	Come visit me again sometime!
***Benutz** bitte deine Kopfhörer!*	Please use your headphones.
***Gib** nicht auf!*	Don't give up!
***Seid** bitte ruhig!*	Please be quiet!
***Holt** mich bitte vom Bahnhof ab!*	Please pick me up from the station.
***Trinkt** nicht zu viel!*	Don't drink too much!
***Erlauben** Sie mir bitte eine Frage!*	Allow me one question, please.
***Helfen** Sie mir!*	Help me!
***Rufen** Sie mich morgen an!*	Call me tomorrow.
***Ärgern** wir uns nicht!*	Let's not get worked up.
***Freuen** wir uns!*	Let's be happy.
***Lass uns** feiern!*	Let's celebrate!
***Lasst uns** tanzen gehen!*	Let's go dancing!

GERMAN VERB	ENGLISH	GERMAN VERB	ENGLISH
benutzen	(to) use	(sich) ärgern	(to) be worked up, (to) get angry
aufgeben	(to) give up		
abholen	(to) pick up, (to) collect	(sich) freuen	(to) be glad
erlauben	(to) allow	feiern	(to) celebrate
helfen	(to) help	tanzen	(to) dance

GENERAL VOCABULARY	ENGLISH	GENERAL VOCABULARY	ENGLISH
mal [*part.*]	*particle for emphasis*	ruhig [*adj.*]	quiet
wieder [*adv.*]	again	(der) Bahnhof [*n.*]	(train) station
(der) Kopfhörer [*n.*]	headphones	(die) Frage [*n.*]	question

14.1 DIE DREI IMPERATIVFORMEN IM DEUTSCHEN
THE THREE IMPERATIVE FORMS IN GERMAN

The **imperative** mood (as opposed to the indicative mood — such as statements) is used for **giving orders** or **instructing** people to do things. In English there are two types of imperatives, depending on who is being told to do – or not to do – something:

- The **"You" command** is used when one or several people are being given an order. In English, the infinitive form (dictionary form) is used for this, and the command may be softened by adding 'please':

  (Please) *clean up* your room!
  Do not come here (, please)!

- The **"We" command** addresses oneself as well as other people around the person speaking. The phrase 'let's' is used, together with the infinitive form of the verb:

  Let's go to the beach!
  Let's celebrate!

In German, however, there are **three** grammatical forms to build the imperative, depending on who is being spoken to.

As in English, the verb is in the first position of the sentence, but an exclamation mark is generally used after every command in German. If the imperative of a verb with separable prefix is being formed, the separated prefix goes at the end of the sentence.

Zu Risiken und Nebenwirkungen lesen Sie die Packungsbeilage und fragen Sie Ihren Arzt oder Apotheker

The following table lists these three imperative types, together with the respective example sentences from the introductory section and notes about their usage and application:

Type of Imperative	Examples	Application
The imperative singular (informal):	*Besuch mich mal wieder!* *Benutz bitte deine Kopfhörer!* *Gib nicht auf!*	• addresses one person Formed by using the stem of the verb without any endings (but including a vowel shift for the irregular verb *geben*; Cf. 'Exceptions' in section 14.3): besuch-en → Besuch! benutz-en → Benutz! aufgeb-en → Gib auf!
The imperative plural (informal):	*Seid bitte ruhig!* *Holt mich bitte vom Bahnhof ab!* *Trinkt nicht zu viel!*	• addresses several people Same verb form as the 2nd person plural in the present tense. The informal pronoun *'ihr'* is dropped: sein → Seid! abholen → Holt ab! trinken → Trinkt!
The imperative singular and plural (formal):	*Erlauben Sie mir bitte eine Frage!* *Helfen Sie mir!* *Rufen Sie mich morgen an!*	• addresses one or more persons formally Same verb form as the 3rd person plural in the present tense. The formal pronoun *'Sie'* comes right after the imperative verb: erlauben → Erlauben Sie! helfen → Helfen Sie! anrufen → Rufen Sie an!

As you can see, German differentiates between the **singular** and **plural** imperative in the **informal** address (i.e., towards people you know well, family, friends, etc.). The **formal** imperative, however, is directed towards unfamiliar people or authority persons and is formed in the same way in both the singular and plural.

14.2 WEITERE FORMULIERUNGEN MIT IMPERATIVER BEDEUTUNG
OTHER EXPRESSIONS WITH IMPERATIVE MEANING

Apart from the three imperative forms outlined above, we often make use of a couple of constructions that also convey commands, orders, or encouragement to do or not to do something. These constructions are not imperatives in a strictly grammatical sense, but they do express the same meaning. In English, they are best translated using the "We"-imperative with "let's …".

The "We" imperative	*Ärgern wir uns nicht!* *Freuen wir uns!*	• includes the person speaking along with other people. Same verb form as the 1st person plural in the present tense. The pronoun 'wir' comes right after the imperative verb: (sich) ärgern → Ärgern wir uns! (sich) freuen → Freuen wir uns!

Another alternative construction that uses a literal translation of the English "let's …" is also possible. Here, however, we need to distinguish between the **singular** (*Lass uns …*) and the **plural** form (*Lasst uns …*). The singular includes the speaker and **one** other person to whom the command or encouragement is being given. The plural form includes the speaker, as well as **several** other people:

Alternative "We" imperative	*Lass uns feiern!*	• includes the person speaking along with **one** other person Stem of the verb *'lassen'* (to let) + accusative form of *'wir'* (= *'uns'*) lassen → Lass uns!
	Lasst uns tanzen gehen!	• includes the person speaking along with **several** other people Same verb form as the 2nd person plural in the present tense + accusative form of *'wir'* (= *'uns'*) lassen → Lasst uns!

14.3 AUSNAHMEN
EXCEPTIONS

Although there are not many exceptions to the rules outlined in the above tables, there are still a few things you need to bear in mind:

- Verbs ending in **-eln** or **-ern** and verbs whose stem ends in **-d**, **-t**, **-ig**, or **consonant + m** require an **-e** to be added to the informal imperative singular:

  sammeln → Sammle!   *wandern → Wandere!*
  (to collect)   (to hike)
  finden → Finde!   *bieten → Biete!*
  (to find)   (to bid; to provide)
  beruhigen → Beruhige!   *atmen → Atme!*
  (to soothe)   (to breathe)

- Many irregular verbs form the informal imperative singular with an *i*, even though they have an *e* as their stem vowel:

  *essen → **Iss!***   *empfehlen → **Empfiehl!***
  *geben → **Gib!***   *lesen → **Lies!***

ÜBUNGEN
EXERCISES

Ü 14.1) Complete the following sentences using the formal imperative form of the verb. One example has been given.

Example:

_____ Sie mich bitte _____! (anrufen) → Rufen Sie mich bitte an!

a) _____ Sie bitte das Fenster _____! (zumachen)

b) Herr und Frau Müller, _____ Sie bitte zur Rezeption! (kommen)

c) _____ Sie bitte langsamer! (sprechen)

d) _____ Sie bitte beim Verlassen des Raumes das Licht _____! (ausschalten)

e) Liebe Gäste, _____ Sie bitte ihre eigene Bettwäsche _____! (mitbringen)

Ü 14.2) Now turn all the formal imperatives from the above exercise into informal ones, according to the example.

Example:

Rufen Sie mich bitte an!   →   Ruf mich bitte an!

a) _____

b) _____

c) _____

d) _____

e) _____

Ü 14.3) Give commands or encouragement to the following people to carry out the activity expressed in each sentence. Use a construction other than the 'normal' three imperative forms. One example has been provided:

Example:

Sag Peter, dass ihr schwimmen gehen sollt!   →   Peter, gehen wir schwimmen! /
Peter, lass uns schwimmen gehen!

a) Sag Karin und Anna, dass ihr einkaufen gehen sollt!

_____

b) Sag Dieter, dass ihr jetzt schlafen sollt!

_____

c) Sag Herrn und Frau Scholz, dass ihr jetzt essen sollt!

_____

d) Sag Paul, dass ihr aufräumen sollt!

_____

e) Sag Wolfgang, dass ihr Katrin vom Bahnhof abholen sollt!

_____

KAPITEL 15 — DER KONJUNKTIV I

CHAPTER 15 - THE KONJUNKTIV I

The German subjunctive mood is called **Konjunktiv**. The *Konjunktiv* helps us express wishes, possibilities, non-factual matters, hearsay, and indirect speech. While the English subjunctive is only rarely used nowadays, the German *Konjunktiv* remains a frequently used verb mood. There are two types of *Konjunktiv* and in this chapter we will focus on the *Konjunktiv I*, which is mainly used in **indirect speech**.

 Study the sentences below, which are all examples of indirect speech and thus contain the *Konjunktiv I*:

*Peter sagte, er **fahre** nach Hause.*	Peter said he was going home.
*Bernd sagte, er **besitze** viele Autos.*	Bernd said he owned many cars.
*Ingo sagte, er **sei** letztes Jahr nach Berlin gefahren.*	Ingo said he went to Berlin last year.
*Paul sagt, er **habe** sich verletzt.*	Paul says he got injured.
*Ina und Willi erklärten, sie **seien** letztes Jahr nach Leipzig umgezogen.*	Ina and Willi explained that they had moved to Leipzig last year.
*Ich sagte, **dass** ich mich hier nicht **auskenne**.*	I said that I didn't know my way around here.
*Julia sagte, **dass** sie die Prüfung bestanden **habe**.*	Julia said that she had passed the exam.
*Ralf fragte, **ob** Peter hier der Chef **sei**.*	Ralf asked whether Peter was the boss here.

GERMAN VERB	ENGLISH	GERMAN VERB	ENGLISH
besitzen	(to) own	umziehen	(to) move, (to) relocate
(sich) verletzen	(to) injure oneself	(sich) auskennen	(to) know one's way
erklären	(to) explain	bestehen	(to) pass (an exam)

GENERAL VOCABULARY	ENGLISH	GENERAL VOCABULARY	ENGLISH
viele [*adj.*]	many	(die) Prüfung [*n.*]	test, exam
hier [*adv.*]	here	(der) Chef [*n.*]	boss, manager

15.1 DER KONJUNKTIV I UND DIE INDIREKTE REDE
THE KONJUNKTIV I AND INDIRECT SPEECH

As already mentioned in the introduction to this chapter, the *Konjunktiv I* is primarily used for expressing things in indirect speech. The most common place where this construction can be encountered is in the newspaper, on TV news, in other forms of media, or wherever a report of somebody else's statement is required.

Indirect speech means that another person's statement is being reported. The original statement usually takes place in **direct speech** and is set in quotation marks:

> Peter sagte: „Ich fahre nach Hause."
> (Peter said, "I'm going home".)

This sentence can be rendered in indirect speech by dropping the quotation marks and putting the verb *'fahren'* in the *Konjunktiv I*:

> Peter sagte, er fahre nach Hause.
> (Peter said he was going home.)

Some pronouns and possessive adjectives also need to be changed in order to reflect the change of speaker ('*Ich*' → '*er*').

In **English**, rather than using a subjunctive form, the verb tense of the original direct speech usually shifts one tense further into the past in indirect speech:

Bernd said, "I **own** many cars".   →   Bernd said he **owned** many cars.
     ⌐→ simple present   ⌐→ simple past

Ingo said, "I **went** to Berlin last year".   →   Ingo said he **had gone** to Berlin last year.
     ⌐→ simple past   ⌐→ past perfect

In **German**, however, certain inflections are applied to the verb to mark it as a *Konjunktiv I* in indirect speech:

Bernd sagte: „Ich besitze viele Autos."   →   *Bernd sagte, er **besitze** viele Autos.*

Ingo sagte:
„Ich bin letztes Jahr nach Berlin gefahren."   →   *Ingo sagte, er **sei** letztes Jahr nach Berlin gefahren.*

The next section explains the required verb endings and conjugations in more detail.

15.2 DIE KONSTRUKTION DES KONJUNKTIV I
CONSTRUCTING THE KONJUNKTIV I

To construct the different forms of the *Konjunktiv I Präsens*, both regular and irregular verbs add the following endings to their verb stem:

	ENDING	REGULAR VERB: *leben*		IRREGULAR VERB: *lesen*	
1st **person** (sing.)	*-e*	*ich*	**lebe**	*ich*	**lese**
2nd **person** (sing.)	*-est*	*du*	**lebest**	*du*	**lesest**
3rd **person** (sing.)	*-e*	*er/sie/es*	**lebe**	*er/sie/es*	**lese**
1st **person** (pl.)	*-en*	*wir*	**leben**	*wir*	**lesen**
2nd **person** (pl.)	*-et*	*ihr*	**lebet**	*ihr*	**leset**
3rd **person** (pl.)	*-en*	*sie*	**leben**	*sie*	**lesen**
Formal (sing. & pl.)	*-en*	*Sie*	**leben**	*Sie*	**lesen**

As you can see, irregular verbs do not undergo a stem vowel change like they normally would, for instance, in the present tense conjugation. The *Konjunktiv I* of **sein**, however, is irregular in that it does not add an -*e* in the 1st and 3rd person singular:

	ENDING	sein	
1st person (sing.)	**-**	*ich*	**sei**
2nd person (sing.)	**-est**	*du*	**sei(e)st**
3rd person (sing.)	**-**	*er/sie/es*	**sei**
1st person (pl.)	**-en**	*wir*	**seien**
2nd person (pl.)	**-et**	*ihr*	**seiet**
3rd person (pl.)	**-en**	*sie*	**seien**
Formal (sing. & pl.)	**-en**	*Sie*	**seien**

In instances where the direct speech is in the **Präteritum** or **Perfekt**, we use the *Konjunktiv I* of *haben* or *sein*, together with the past participle form of the relevant verb:

DIRECT SPEECH	INDIRECT SPEECH
Paul sagt: „Ich habe mich verletzt."	*Paul sagt, er **habe** sich **verletzt**.*
Ina und Willi erklärten: „Wir sind letztes Jahr nach Leipzig umgezogen."	*Ina und Willi erklärten, sie **seien** letztes Jahr nach Leipzig **umgezogen**.*

A very common alternative construction for reporting statements in indirect speech employs the subordinating conjunction **dass**, which introduces a subclause containing the reported statement. In such a construction, the verb in the *Konjunktiv I* is placed at the end of the subclause:

DIRECT SPEECH	INDIRECT SPEECH
Ich sagte: „Ich kenne mich hier nicht aus."	*Ich sagte, **dass** ich mich hier nicht **auskenne**.*
Julia sagte: „Ich habe die Prüfung bestanden"	*Julia sagte, **dass** sie die Prüfung bestanden **habe**.*

If we need to report a **W-question** in indirect speech, the question word is retained at the beginning of the subclause, while the verb in the *Konjunktiv I* goes at the end of the subclause:

Ralf fragte: „Wer ist hier der Chef?"	*Ralf fragte, **wer** hier der Chef **sei**.*

Yes-or-no-questions, however, require the subordinating conjunction **ob**. The word order remains the same as with W-questions:

Ralf fragte: „Ist Peter hier der Chef?"	*Ralf fragte,* **ob** *Peter hier der Chef* **sei***.*

Also, note that subclauses are always separated from the main clause by a **comma**.

15.3 DEN KONJUNKTIV I DURCH ANDERE FORMEN ERSETZEN
REPLACING THE KONJUNKTIV I WITH ALTERNATIVE FORMS

In general, the above rules regarding indirect speech and the associated use of the *Konjunktiv I* are always applicable. There are, however, situations where the *Konjunktiv I* form is identical to the verb in the indicative. To better accentuate the nature of reporting in such instances, the *Konjunktiv I* is usually replaced with the *Konjunktiv II* form:

DIRECT SPEECH	INDIRECT SPEECH
Ich sagte: „Ich gehe heute schwimmen".	*Ich sagte, ich* **gehe** *heute schwimmen.* ↓ Konjunktiv I is identical with indicative ↓ *Ich sagte, ich* **ginge** *heute schwimmen.* ↓ Konjunktiv II form

The next chapter will discuss the *Konjunktiv II* and its formation in more detail. Apart from the *Konjunktiv II*, there are other ways in which the *Konjunktiv I* is frequently replaced, especially in colloquial German. This has to do with the fact that the *Konjunktiv I* is often perceived as somewhat stilted and old-fashioned. Alternative forms that are possible in contemporary German include:

- *dass* + indicative   →   *Ich sagte,* **dass** *ich heute schwimmen* **gehe***.*
- the indicative   →   *Ich sagte, ich* **gehe** *heute schwimmen.*
- würden + infinitive   →   *Ich sagte, ich* **würde** *heute schwimmen* **gehen***.*
- *dass* + Konjunktiv II   →   *Ich sagte,* **dass** *ich heute schwimmen* **ginge***.*

ÜBUNGEN
EXERCISES

Ü 15.1) The following sentences contain direct speech. Convert them into sentences in indirect speech using the *Konjunktiv I*. One example has been given.

Example:
Anke sagte: „Ich koche heute Spaghetti." → Anke sagte, sie koche heute Spaghetti.

a) Peter sagte: „Ich stehe morgens nicht gerne auf."

_____

b) Anna und Tom sagten: „Wir fahren am Sonntag in den Urlaub".

_____

c) Herr Schuster erklärte: „Ich habe bei der Bank einen Kredit aufgenommen."

_____

d) Inge schimpfte: „Ihr habt euer Zimmer wieder nicht aufgeräumt!"

_____

Ü 15.2) The following sentences contain indirect speech using the *Konjunktiv I*. Convert them back to the original direct speech. One example has been provided.

Example:
Der Lehrer sagte, er sei sehr zufrieden mit den Schülern.
→ Der Lehrer sagte: „Ich bin sehr zufrieden mit den Schülern."

a) Frau Acker berichtete, sie habe einen schönen Urlaub gehabt.

_____

b) Olaf sagte, er freue sich auf die große Party.

_____

c) Paul sagte, ihr habet Glück mit dem Wetter gehabt.

_____

d) Ich fragte, warum er noch nicht umgezogen sei.

_____

Ü 15.3) Now use the sentences from Ü 15.2 and replace the standard indirect speech with an alternative (colloquial) indirect speech form. There are several possibilities.

a) _____

b) _____

c) _____

d) _____

KAPITEL 16 — DER KONJUNKTIV II
CHAPTER 16 - THE KONJUNKTIV II

The **Konjunktiv II** is the second type of subjunctive mood in German. It is generally the more frequently used one out of the two and has a broader range of usage scenarios. While forming sentences in indirect speech is the primary purpose of the *Konjunktiv I*, the *Konjunktiv II* is used to talk about **hypothetical** or **contrary-to-fact** situations, as well as **wishes** and **conditions**. While this type of subjunctive does exist in English, it is still more commonly used in German and encompasses a larger set of application scenarios there.

 The following sentences use the *Konjunktiv II* to highlight a number of these hypothetical scenarios.

Ich **wünschte**, mein Auto **verbrauchte** nicht so viel Benzin.	I wish my car wouldn't use so much fuel.
Ich **hätte** gerne einen Hund.	I would love to have a dog.
Wenn ich du **wäre**, **würde** ich meine Hausaufgaben sofort erledigen.	If I were you, I would do my homework immediately.
Könnten Sie bitte hier nicht rauchen?	Could you please not smoke here?
Wenn ich das **wollte**, dann **würde** ich es dir sagen.	If I wanted that, then I would tell you.
Wenn der Rasenmäher **funktionierte**, **könnten** wir den Rasen mähen.	If the lawnmower worked, we could mow the grass.
Ach, **wäre** er doch langsamer gefahren!	Oh my, if only he had driven more slowly!

GERMAN VERB	ENGLISH	GERMAN VERB	ENGLISH
verbrauchen erledigen rauchen	(to) consume, (to) use up (to) do, (to) get done (to) smoke	funktionieren mähen	(to) work, (to) function (to) mow, (to) cut

GENERAL VOCABULARY	ENGLISH	GENERAL VOCABULARY	ENGLISH
(das) Benzin [*n.*]	gas, petrol, fuel	(der) Rasen [*n.*]	lawn, grass
(der) Hund [*n.*]	dog	Ach! [*interj.*]	Alas!
(die) Hausaufgaben [*n. pl.*]	homework	doch [*part.*]	*particle for emphasis*
(der) Rasenmäher [*n.*]	lawnmower	langsamer [*adv.*]	more slowly

16.1 DER KONJUNKTIV II UND DER ENGLISCHE SUBJUNKTIV IM VERGLEICH
THE KONJUNKTIV II AND THE ENGLISH SUBJUNCTIVE IN COMPARISON

In **English**, the **subjunctive mood** is somewhat of a dying breed. Though still in use, there is quite a narrow set of usage scenarios where the English subjunctive is still regularly employed. Furthermore, the English subjunctive form is harder to recognize than the German one, as it only appears in either the dictionary form of the verb, or it looks just like the simple past tense.

The most common situations in which you can still encounter the English subjunctive include:

- **If-clauses** in nonfactual sentences. Here, the subjunctive form of '(to) be' looks like the simple past form 'were'.

    "If you **were** a better friend, you would visit me more often."

    ↳ Subjunctive form of 'to be' → Contrary-to-fact: the person apparently is not a good friend.

- **Wishful** statements. Here, the introductory verb ('I *wish* …') is followed by the subjunctive form of the relevant verb in the simple past.

    "I wish I **had** told him the truth."

    ↳ Subjunctive form of 'to have'. Not real → the person was never told the truth.

- After expressions that **urge**, **demand**, **ask**, or express **necessity**. In such a scenario the subjunctive appears as the infinitive form of the relevant verb.

    "He demanded that I **call** him immediately."
    "It is vital that they **stay** inside."

    ↳ Subjunctive forms identical with the **infinitive**.
    A strong need or request is being expressed.

The **German *Konjunktiv II***, just like the English subjunctive, helps us describe nonfactual matters, hypothetical situations, or wishful thinking. However, it may also be used to add a sense of politeness to what is being said or to express conditions. It derives its form from the *Präteritum* tense but comes with its own set of endings and vowel shifts, particularly for irregular verbs. The following section will explain how the German *Konjunktiv II* is formed.

16.2 DIE KONSTRUKTION DES KONJUNKTIV II
CONSTRUCTING THE KONJUNKTIV II

The *Konjunktiv II* conjugation for **regular verbs** is the same as for the *Präteritum*. Thus, all you need to do is add the following endings to the verb stem:

	ENDING	EXAMPLE	
1st person (sing.)	*-te*	*ich*	*lebte*
2nd person (sing.)	*-test*	*du*	*lebtest*
3rd person (sing.)	*-te*	*er/sie/es*	*lebte*
1st person (pl.)	*-ten*	*wir*	*lebten*
2nd person (pl.)	*-tet*	*ihr*	*lebtet*
3rd person (pl.)	*-ten*	*sie*	*lebten*
Formal (sing. & pl.)	*-ten*	*Sie*	*lebten*

*Ich **wünschte**, mein Auto **verbrauchte** nicht so viel Benzin.*

Konjunktiv II forms are indistinguishable from their *Präteritum* forms.

16.2.1 Irregular Verbs

Irregular verbs of the *Konjunktiv II* using the **stem** for the *Präteritum* and the endings are listed below. Additionally, all verb stems containing a vowel in the *Präteritum* undergo a vowel shift to the respective **Umlaut**. Thus, the frequently used verbs *haben*, *sein*, *werden*, as well as *bleiben* are conjugated as follows:

	ENDING	haben	sein	werden	bleiben
Präteritum stem		hatt-	war-	wurd-	blieb-
1st person (sing.) 2nd person (sing.) 3rd person (sing.)	e -(e)st e	ich **hätte** du **hättest** er/sie/ **hätte** es	ich **wäre** du **wärest** er/sie **wäre** es	ich **würde** du **würdest** er/sie/ **würde** es	ich **bliebe** du **bliebest** er/sie/ **bliebe** es
1st person (pl.) 2nd person (pl.) 3rd person (pl.) Formal (sing. & pl.)	-en -(e)t -en -en	wir **hätten** ihr **hättet** sie **hätten** Sie **hätten**	wir **wären** ihr **wäret** sie **wären** Sie **wären**	wir **würden** ihr **würdet** sie **würden** Sie **würden**	wir **blieben** ihr **bliebet** sie **blieben** Sie **blieben**

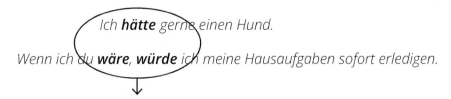

Ich **hätte** gerne einen Hund.

Wenn ich du **wäre**, **würde** ich meine Hausaufgaben sofort erledigen.

Konjunktiv II of irregular verbs, conveying wishful thinking / nonfactual scenarios.

16.2.2 Modal Verbs

Modal verbs form their *Konjunktiv II* by retaining their **infinitive stem** and adding the regular **Konjunktiv-II-endings** on to the stem. The only exception to this is the modal *mögen*, which has a slightly changed stem:

	dürfen	können	müssen	sollen	wollen	mögen
ich	dürfte	könnte	müsste	sollte	wollte	möchte
du	dürftest	könntest	müsstest	solltest	wolltest	möchtest
er/sie/es	dürfte	könnte	müsste	sollte	wollte	möchte
wir	dürften	könnten	müssten	sollten	wollten	möchten
ihr	dürftet	könntet	müsstet	solltet	wolltet	möchtet
sie/Sie	dürften	können	müssten	sollten	wollten	möchten

Könnten Sie bitte hier nicht rauchen?

> *Konjunktiv II* of *können*. Used here to form a polite request.

*Wenn ich das **wollte**, dann **würde** ich es dir sagen.*

> *Konjunktiv II* of *wollen*. Used here to talk about a hypothetical situation → the 'wanting' is not actual.

16.3 DER GEBRAUCH DES KONJUNKTIV II
THE USAGE OF THE KONJUNKTIV II

As already mentioned, the German *Konjunktiv II* is primarily used in scenarios that are contrary to the facts or where wishful thinking is being expressed. Below we summarize the most important scenarios:

- **Hypothetical scenarios**

  *Wenn der Rasenmäher **funktionierte**, **könnten** wir den Rasen mähen.*

  → Expresses a hypothetical situation that is currently unattainable.

- **Sentences with conditional meaning.**

  *Wenn ich du **wäre**, **würde** ich das nicht machen.*

  → Nonfactual situation, tied to a condition ('If I were you …'). Such sentences are often introduced by "*wenn*" (if) or phrases like "*Wenn ich du wäre*" (If I were you) / "*An deiner Stelle*" (In your position).

- **To express politeness**

  ***Dürfte** ich kurz deinen Computer benutzen?*

  → Adds a sense of politeness to requests. Often associated with a modal verb in the *Konjunktiv II*.

- **To express wishes**

  *Ach, **wäre** er doch langsamer gefahren!*

  → Wishful thinking. Wishes expressed in the past tense (*Konjunktiv II* of auxiliary verb + past participle of main verb) are unfulfillable and therefore often convey a sense of regret.

· **In indirect speech**

*Ich sagte ihm, ich **hätte** es versucht.*

→ To replace the *Konjunktiv I* in indirect speech if it is identical with the indicative form of the verb. Thus, the reported nature of the sentence can be conveyed better.

16.4 DEN KONJUNKTIV II DURCH WÜRDE + INFINITIV ERSETZEN
REPLACING THE KONJUNKTIV II WITH WÜRDE + INFINITIVE

There are instances where the *Konjunktiv II* form of a verb is identical with its indicative *Präteritum* form. To avoid confusion in these situations, we usually replace the *Konjunktiv II* with a construction consisting of **würde + the infinitive**:

*Wenn du meine Frage **beantwortetest**, könnte ich dir helfen.*
↓
Konjunktiv II form identical with *Präteritum* indicative form
↓
*Wenn du meine Frage **beantworten würdest**, könnte ich dir helfen.*

Another reason why this construction is sometimes preferable, especially in spoken German, has to do with the fact that a number of verbs tend to sound old-fashioned when put in the *Konjunktiv II*. A few common verbs that do not frequently form the *Konjunktiv II* anymore include:

VERB	'OLD' KONJUNKTIV II	KONJUNKTIV II REPLACEMENT
essen (to eat)	äße	würde essen
fahren (to drive)	führe	würde fahren
gewinnen (to win)	gewönne	würde gewinnen
helfen (to help)	hülfe	würde helfen
lügen (to lie)	löge	würde lügen
riechen (to smell)	röche	würde riechen
schaffen (to accomplish)	schüfe	würde schaffen
schieben (to push, to shove)	schöbe	würde schieben
schließen (to close)	schlösse	würde schließen
sprechen (to speak)	spräche	würde sprechen
waschen (to wash)	wüsche	würde waschen

However, please do not make it too easy for yourself. Even though the replacement with *würde* + infinitive is correct and sometimes even unavoidable, it is not a very elegant way to express yourself in German. Try to use the *Konjunktiv II* wherever possible.

ÜBUNGEN
EXERCISES

Ü 16.1) Complete the conjugations of the following verbs in the *Konjunktiv II*.

	lieben	können	mögen	heißen	sehen	werden
ich	liebte					
du						würdest
er/sie/es				hieße		
wir		könnten				
ihr					sähet	
sie/Sie			möchten			

Ü 16.2) Some people need your advice. Use the *Konjunktiv II* form of the verbs in brackets to suggest to people what you would do in their position. You may use the phrase '*An deiner Stelle...*' to start the sentence. One example has been given.

Example: "Ich habe Angst vor dem Fliegen." (Schlaftablette im Flugzeug nehmen)
→ An deiner Stelle nähme ich eine Schlaftablette im Flugzeug.

a) „Die Party ist langweilig." (nach Hause gehen)

_____

b) „Ich habe kein Geld." (mehr arbeiten)

_____

c) „Mein Hund ist krank." (zum Tierarzt bringen)

_____

d) „Morgen regnet es den ganzen Tag." (zu Hause bleiben)

_____

e) „Ich weiß nicht, was ich werden soll, wenn ich groß bin." (Lehrer werden)

_____

Ü 16.3) Now use your solutions from Ü 16.2 to re-write them with the _würde_ + infinitive replacement instead of the _Konjunktiv II._

a) _____

b) _____

c) _____

d) _____

e) _____

SCHLUSSWORT
CONCLUSION

Congratulations on making it to the end of this workbook! By working through the different chapters, you have gained a solid understanding of the way in which verbs behave. You understand how they interact with other parts of speech and what their importance is in constructing meaningful sentences. Amongst other things, you are now able to express yourself in all the different German tenses, you know how to switch between the active and passive voice, you can confidently give commands in German, and by employing indirect speech you are able to report what others have said. You also know how to express wishes and hypothetical scenarios using the *Konjunktiv* mood.

Do bear in mind, however, that all the above things require practice, and the more exposure you have to the language, the more natural your command of the various verb phenomena and other aspects of the German language will become. This is best achieved by actually spending time in a German-speaking country while listening to and interacting with German native-speakers. However, since we know that an extended stay abroad is not always a viable option, we would like to provide you with a few tips, resources, and suggestions which you may find helpful for your language studies:

- Learning a language from a coursebook is certainly great for starting out and for gaining a basic understanding of its underlying rules. However, fluency comes through engaging with native speakers and through picking up and assimilating the way they use the language (after all, this is how you became fluent in your first language as a child). Try finding a German tandem language partner (in-person or online) who will teach you their language from a native speaker's angle!

- Read and listen! The next best thing to real-life interaction is exposure to the language through various media. Alongside books that interest you, why not watch your favourite show or movie in German? You can always turn on the subtitles, but over time you should notice how your reliance on them will gradually decrease.

- Use online resources! There are several public German broadcasters whose websites offer news stories and a variety of coverage in simplified German – both written and as audio content! For example:

  www.ard-digital.de/inklusion/einfache-und-leichte-sprache
  www.dw.com/de/deutsch-lernen/nachrichten/s-8030

- A good resource for finding more materials on German culture and language learning is the Goethe Institut, which has an international presence in many countries. This is their German website, but you may also want to look up their website in your country:

www.goethe.de/de/index.html

And on that note, we bid you *Auf Wiedersehen* and wish you *viel Erfolg und alles Gute!*

LÖSUNGSSCHLÜSSEL
ANSWER KEY

UNIT 1

Ü 1.1)

Ich hoffe, dir geht es gut. Ich freue mich schon auf **nächste** Woche! Es ist schon so lange her, dass wir uns gesehen haben. Falls **möglich**, nehme ich am Montag den **frühen** Zug, damit ich nicht so **spät** ankomme. **Könntest** du mich bitte vom Bahnhof abholen? Das Taxi ist immer so **unverschämt** teuer. Ich bringe auch **Weihnachtsgebäck** mit! Also dann, bis bald und liebe **Grüße**!

Ü 1.2)

INFINITIVE	PRESENT PARTICIPLE	PAST PARTICIPLE
fahren, sehen, erkennen, lesen, abnehmen, lenken	erklärend, erzählend, ablenkend, verteilend, verstehend	geklettert, gesungen, geraucht, geleert, gejuckt, gegossen, gerannt

Ü 1.3)

Indikativ: Mood of a verb used to formulate factual statements or questions.

Konjunktiv I: One of the German subjunctive moods. Primarily used in the construction of indirect speech.

Konjunktiv II: One of the German subjunctive moods. Primarily used to express hypothetical events or wishes.

Imperativ: Mood of a verb used to express commands given to one or more people.

Ü 1.4)

	Voice:
a) Das Buch **wird gelesen**.	Passive
b) Der Mann **wartete** seit Stunden auf den Zug.	Active
c) Wir **haben** einen großen Balkon.	Active
d) Das alte Klavier **wurde** über die Jahre hinweg viel **gespielt**.	Passive
e) In der Schweiz **werden** hauptsächlich drei Sprachen **gesprochen**.	Passive
f) Die gesprochenen Sprachen **sind** Deutsch, Französisch und Italienisch.	Active

Ü 2.1)

a) Peter kann nicht arbeiten.

b) Sandra kann nicht arbeiten.

c) Wir können nicht arbeiten.

d) Du kannst nicht arbeiten.

e) Herr Müller kann nicht arbeiten.

f) Ihr könnt nicht arbeiten.

Ü 2.2)

a) Wir **wollen** heute Nachmittag Fußball spielen.

b) Du **darfst** hier nicht so laut reden.

c) Ich **muss** zuhause immer Hausschuhe tragen.

d) Mein kleiner Bruder **kann** nicht Fahrrad fahren.

e) Wir **sollen** uns im Urlaub ausruhen.

f) Möchtest du morgen zu mir kommen?

Ü 2.3)

a) Peter kann Klavier spielen.

b) Sandra und Erika müssen nach Hause gehen.

c) Wir dürfen heute ein Konzert besuchen.

d) Ich will ein Auto kaufen.

e) Hans und Frank möchten Musik hören.

Ü 2.4)

a) (6) desire   **d)** (3) ability

b) (1) permission   **e)** (2) aptness

c) (5) desire   **f)** (4) necessity

Ü 3.1)

a) Meine Wohnung **ist** in München.	MV
b) Ich **habe** einen Brief **bekommen**.	AV
c) Hoffentlich **wird** das Wetter schön.	MV
d) Mein Vater **ist** letztes Jahr **gestorben**.	AV
e) Wir **haben** zwei Katzen und einen Hund.	MV
f) Das Auto **wird gestartet**.	AV
g) Ich **bin** gestern nach Hause **gekommen**.	AV
h) Wirst du mich nächste Woche **besuchen**?	AV

Ü 3.2)

a) Ich **bin** gestern 2 Kilometer gelaufen.

b) Er **hat** das Buch nicht gelesen.

c) Wir **haben** letzte Woche den neuen James-Bond-Film gesehen.

d) Seid ihr mit dem Bus gefahren?

e) Das Flugzeug **ist** gelandet.

f) Sie **hat / haben** dich nicht verstanden.

Ü 3.3)

a) Das Auto wird gestartet.

b) Der Bus wird gefahren.

c) Die Männer werden gesehen.

d) Das Haus wird gekauft.

Ü 4.1)

SEPARABLE	INSEPARABLE	PAST PARTICIPLE
einschlafen		eingeschlafen
	gestehen	gestanden
anziehen		angezogen
umsehen		umgesehen
	verlieren	verloren
zumachen		zugemacht
	befolgen	befolgt
	verachten	verachtet
weggehen		weggegangen
	verhaften	verhaftet
aufhören		aufgehört
	empfehlen	empfohlen

Ü 4.2)

E.g.: absehen, ansehen, aussehen, einsehen, fernsehen, hersehen, hellsehen, nachsehen, übersehen, zusehen, vorsehen, aufsehen, besehen, durchsehen, gegenübersehen, herabsehen, hinaufsehen, hinsehen, hineinsehen, reinsehen, umsehen, wegsehen, fortsehen, heraussehen, hinterhersehen, hochsehen, voraussehen, vorbeisehen, weitersehen, wiedersehen, zurücksehen …

Ü 4.3)

a) Was kaufst du ein?

b) Ich habe gestern verschlafen.

c) Peter, räum dein Zimmer auf!

d) Klaus, bezahl deine Miete!

e) Verkaufst du dein Haus?

f) Erkennst du ihn?

g) Gib mir mein Buch zurück!

Ü 5.1)

Plusquamperfekt - Past perfect; Präteritum - Simple past; Perfekt - Present perfect; Präsens - Present tense; Futur II - Future perfect; Futur I - Future tense

Ü 5.2)

A time expression, such as *gerade*, *momentan*, or *im Augenblick* is added to the sentence to emphasize the ongoing nature of the action.

Ü 5.3)

The *Plusquamperfekt*, the *Perfekt*, the *Futur I*, and the *Futur II* are compound tenses in German.

Ü 5.4)

a) Präsens

b) Futur I

c) Perfekt

d) Perfekt

e) Präteritum

f) Futur II

g) Plusquamperfekt

h) Präsens

i) Futur I

j) Präsens | Futur II

k) Präteritum

l) Plusquamperfekt | Präteritum

g) Plusquamperfekt

h) Präsens

i) Futur I

j) Präsens | Futur II

k) Präteritum

l) Plusquamperfekt | Präteritum

Ü 6.1)

a) Anna kocht das Abendessen.
     S   P   O

b) Sie gibt ihrem Freund ein Geschenk.
     S   P   O (Dat.)   O (Acc.)

c) Das Haus wird nächstes Jahr gebaut werden.
      S   P   P   P

d) Letztes Jahr hat Peter geheiratet.
                P   S   P

e) Die Miete können wir inzwischen nicht mehr bezahlen.
    O (Acc.)   P   S   P

f) Kannst du deinem Freund Geld geben?
      P   S   O (Dat.)   O (Acc.)   P

Ü 6.2)

a) Die Schüler lesen ein Buch.

b) Werden wir nächstes Jahr ein Haus bauen?

c) Warum möchte Lisa ihrem Freund einen Rat geben?

d) Nächste Woche verkaufen wir unser Auto einem Freund.

Ü 6.3)

Examples:

Der Mann kocht das Abendessen.

Ihr kocht das Abendessen.

Wir kochen das Abendessen.

Wir bauen nächstes Jahr ein Haus.

Wir kaufen nächstes Jahr ein Haus.

Wir haben ein Haus gekauft.

Wie ist das Abendessen?

Warum haben wir ein Auto gekauft?

Wie kocht der Mann das Abendessen?

Warum haben wir ihr das Auto gegeben?

Wir geben dem Freund das Auto.

Warum bauen wir nächstes Jahr ein Haus? ...

UNIT 2

Ü 7.1)

a) Hallo, wie heißt du?

b) Pedro kommt aus Portugal.

c) Er wohnt seit zwei Jahren in Berlin.

d) Marlene spricht Spanisch, Chinesisch und Deutsch.

e) Was studieren Sie?

f) Frau Meyer arbeitet als Anwältin.

g) Ich lerne seit einem Jahr Deutsch.

h) Was sind Sie von Beruf?

i) Habt ihr auch Hunger?

j) Die Kinder spielen Fußball.

Ü 7.2)

	MACHEN	WOLLEN	TREFFEN	LESEN	WERDEN
ich	mache	will	treffe	lese	werde
du	machst	willst	triffst	liest	wirst
er/sie/es	macht	will	trifft	liest	wird
wir	machen	wollen	treffen	lesen	werden
ihr	macht	wollt	trefft	lest	werdet
sie/Sie	machen	wollen	treffen	lesen	werden

Ü 7.3)

er schläft - schlafen; er trinkt - trinken; er empfiehlt - empfehlen; er muss - müssen; er überlegt - überlegen; er nimmt - nehmen; er lässt - lassen; er lebt - leben; er wird - werden; er isst - essen

Ü 8.1)

a) Wie viele Pfannkuchen hast du gegessen?

b) Im Urlaub bin ich jeden Tag zwei Kilometer am Strand gelaufen.

c) Guten Morgen! Hast du gut geschlafen?

d) Karin wollte nicht auf die Party gehen. Deshalb ist sie zuhause geblieben.

e) Ich habe auf der Party zu viel Alkohol getrunken.

f) Deine Mutter hat vorhin angerufen. Sie wollte mit dir reden.

g) Wir haben kein Auto. Deshalb sind wir mit dem Zug gefahren.

h) Ich habe dir einen Brief geschrieben. Ist er schon angekommen?

i) Schnell! Der Film hat schon begonnen!

Ü 8.2)

a) Ich bin nach Hause gegangen.

b) Maria hat uns gesehen.

c) Ihr habt Spaghetti gegessen.

d) Bist du um neun Uhr eingeschlafen?

e) Habt ihr gestern Fußball gespielt?

f) Onkel Hans hat Medizin studiert.

g) Seid ihr zum Taxistand gelaufen?

h) Mein Großvater ist im Jahr 1995 gestorben.

i) Ich bin nach München gefahren.

Ü 8.3)

a) aufwachen	ich bin aufgewacht	er ist aufgewacht
b) besprechen	ich habe besprochen	er hat besprochen
c) wegfahren	ich bin weggefahren	er ist weggefahren
d) versprechen	ich habe versprochen	er hat versprochen
e) zumachen	ich habe zugemacht	er hat zugemacht
f) aufstehen	ich bin aufgestanden	er ist aufgestanden
g) ablegen	ich habe abgelegt	er hat abgelegt
h) mitbringen	ich habe mitgebracht	er hat mitgebracht

Ü 8.4)

a) Ist er schon aufgestanden?

b) Ich habe das nicht gewusst.

c) Was hast du gesagt?

d) Deine Schwester hat angerufen.

e) Ich habe einen Computer gekauft.

f) Wir sind zum Wochenmarkt gelaufen.

g) Sie ist mit Lufthansa geflogen.

h) Die Kinder sind gewachsen.

i) Die Gäste sind lange geblieben.

j) Das Wetter ist schön geworden.

Ü 9.1)

*Nun **war** das arme Kind in dem großen Wald ganz allein. Da **hatte** es große Angst. Es **wusste** nicht, wo es **war** und **fing** an zu laufen, bis es bald Abend **wurde**. Da **sah** es ein kleines Häuschen und **ging** hinein. In dem Haus **war** alles klein: da **stand** ein Tisch mit sieben kleinen Tellern. Außerdem **gab** es sieben Messer und Gabeln und sieben Becher. An der Wand **standen** sieben Betten. Schneewittchen, weil es so hungrig und durstig **war**, **aß** von jedem Teller ein wenig Gemüse und Brot und **trank** aus jedem Becher einen Tropfen Wein. Dann, weil es so müde **war**, **legte** es sich in ein Bett, aber keins **passte**; das eine **war** zu lang, das andere zu kurz, bis endlich das siebente recht **war**: und darin **blieb** es liegen, **dachte** an den lieben Gott und **schlief** ein.*

Ü 9.2)

INFINITIVE	PRÄTERITUM (1ST PERSON SINGULAR)	TYPE	INFINITIVE	PRÄTERITUM (1ST PERSON SINGULAR)	TYPE
gehen	ging	≠	spielen	spielte	=
fahren	fuhr	≠	sehen	sah	≠
essen	aß	≠	nennen	nannte	+
bleiben	blieb	≠	schreiben	schrieb	≠
arbeiten	arbeitete	=	nehmen	nahm	≠
machen	machte	=	wohnen	wohnte	=
brennen	brannte	+	trinken	trank	≠
kommen	kam	≠	treffen	traf	≠
kaufen	kaufte	=	stehen	stand	≠
hören	hörte	=	sprechen	sprach	≠

Ü 9.3)

a) Ich las ein Buch.

b) Du fuhrst mit dem Bus zur Arbeit.

c) Ich schrieb am Computer.

d) Spracht ihr mit meiner Mutter?

e) Um sieben Uhr traf ich einen Freund.

f) Um zwanzig Uhr gingen wir ins Kino.

g) Wir sahen einen Film mit Tom Hanks.

h) Danach tranken wir noch etwas.

i) Um ein Uhr war er zu Hause.

j) Sahen Sie noch ein bisschen fern?

Ü 9.4)

Ein Lehrer, ein Politiker und ein Anwalt **starben** und **kamen** in den Himmel. St. Peter **war** aber schlecht gelaunt, weil schon so viele Menschen im Himmel **waren** und deshalb **wollte** er es den dreien schwer machen. Als sie ans Tor **kamen, sagte** St. Peter zu ihnen, dass sie nur durch das Bestehen eines Tests in den Himmel kommen **konnten**: Alle drei **mussten** jeweils eine Frage beantworten. St. Peter **wandte** sich also an den Lehrer und **sagte**: „Was **war** der Name des Schiffes, das mit einem Eisberg **kollidierte** und mit all seinen Passagieren **sank**?" Der Lehrer **dachte** einen Moment nach und **antwortete** „Ich glaube, das **war** die Titanic." St. Peter **ließ** ihn durch das Tor. Er **hasste** aber Politiker und **suchte** deshalb nach einer schwierigeren Frage. St. Peter **wandte** sich an den Politiker und **fragte**: „Wie viele Menschen **starben** auf dem Schiff?" Der Politiker **hatte** Glück, weil er ein Buch über die Titanic gelesen hatte. Er **sagte**: „1228". Das **war** richtig und St. Peter **ließ** ihn durch das Tor. Dann **wandte** sich St. Peter an den Anwalt und **fragte**: „Wie **hießen** die Opfer?"

Ü 10.1)

a) Nachdem er nach München **gefahren** war, war er sehr müde.

b) Letztes Jahr zogen wir in die Stadt, in der meine Großeltern **gelebt hatten**.

c) Er **hatte** fünf Bier **getrunken**, als er nach Hause ging.

d) Als mein Chef mich anrief, **war** ich schon nach Hause **gegangen**.

e) Nachdem das Wetter so schlecht **geworden war**, mussten wir die Feier absagen.

Ü 10.2)

a) Nachdem ich zur Arbeit gefahren war, sprach ich mit dem Chef.

b) Nachdem ich mit dem Chef gesprochen hatte, aß ich zu Mittag.

c) Nachdem ich zu Mittag gegessen hatte, rief ich Kunden an.

d) Nachdem ich Kunden angerufen hatte, ging ich nach Hause.

e) Nachdem ich nach Hause gegangen war, sah ich fern.

f) Nachdem ich ferngesehen hatte, schlief ich ein.

Ü 10.3)

a) Gestern **ging** ich mit meiner Freundin auf eine Party.

<u>   Pr   </u>

b) Bevor wir das Haus **verließen**, **hatten** wir noch zu Abend **gegessen**.

<u>   Pr   Ppf   </u>

c) Nachdem uns das Taxi zur Party **gebracht hatte**, **haben** wir unsere Freunde **begrüßt**.

<u>   Ppf   Pf   </u>

d) Wir **hatten** viel Spaß und **blieben** bis zwei Uhr nachts.

<u>   Pr   Pr   </u>

Ü 11.1)

a) Er wird nächsten Monat ein Auto kaufen.

b) Wirst du heute Abend auf die Party gehen?

c) Ihr werdet morgen zur Arbeit gehen müssen.

d) Wirst du nächstes Jahr in Rente gehen?

e) Wir werden später mit dem Chef sprechen.

Ü 11.2)

a) Peter wird wahrscheinlich traurig sein.

b) Ich werde vermutlich mit dem Zug fahren.

c) Es wird wohl nicht lange dauern.

d) Wir werden wahrscheinlich ein Auto kaufen.

e) Ihr werdet wohl mehr Verantwortung übernehmen.

Ü 11.3)

a) Helmut wird am Wochenende ein Buch lesen.

b) Jörg wird am Wochenende in ein Restaurant gehen.

c) Karin und Anna werden am Wochenende zu Hause bleiben.

d) Ich werde am Wochenende Freunde besuchen.

e) Du wirst am Wochenende viel fernsehen.

f) Die Müllers werden am Wochenende eine Party feiern.

g) Katja wird am Wochenende im Büro arbeiten.

h) Opa wird am Wochenende einen Film sehen.

Ü 12.1)

a) Sie wird schon nach Hause gegangen **sein**.

b) Bis dahin werden wir mindestens noch einmal einkaufen gegangen **sein**.

c) In zehn Jahren werde ich in Rente gegangen **sein**.

d) Wenn ihr zurückkommt, werde ich schon das Essen für euch gekocht **haben**.

e) In spätestens einer Stunde wird das Kind eingeschlafen **sein**.

Ü 12.2)

a) Bis dahin werde ich schon wieder aufgewacht sein.

b) Warum wirst du bis morgen deine Arbeit erledigt haben?

c) Nächstes Jahr werden wird zum ersten Mal in den Urlaub gefahren sein.

d) Er wird das wohl gewusst haben.

e) Werden deine Eltern bis sieben Uhr gekocht haben?

Ü 12.3)

a) Außerirdische werden auf der Erde gelandet sein.

b) Das Klima wird wärmer geworden sein.

c) Computer werden die Weltherrschaft übernommen haben.

d) Das Polareis wird geschmolzen sein.

e) Die Kontinente werden im Meer versunken sein.

f) 90% der Menschen werden gestorben sein.

Ü 13.1)

a) Du **wirst** hier noch gebraucht.

b) Ich **werde** jeden Morgen von meiner Frau geweckt.

c) Die Tower Bridge **wird** von Touristen oft besucht.

d) Wir **werden** von deinen Eltern zu ihrer Geburtstagsparty eingeladen.

e) Das Abendessen **wird** ab sechs Uhr serviert.

f) Die Patienten **werden** mit den neuesten Methoden behandelt.

g) **Werdet** ihr von seinen Schwiegereltern abgeholt?

h) Die Handys **werden** im Ausland produziert.

Ü 13.2)

a) Wir haben den Hund gefüttert.

b) Du hast die Teller gewaschen.

c) Der Pilot landet das Flugzeug.

d) Ich rufe euch.

e) Die Mutter badete das Kind.

f) Der Vater wird das Kind loben.

Ü 13.3)

a) Die Katze wird von Klaus gefüttert.

b) Der Computer wird von Klaus benutzt werden.

c) Das Buch war von Inge geschrieben worden.

d) Das Problem wurde den Schülern vom Lehrer erklärt.

e) Der Junge wird vom Vater zum Fußballtraining gefahren.

f) Der Kunde wird von mir angerufen werden.

Ü 13.4)

a) Es wird morgens beim Frühstück Zeitung gelesen.

b) Es wird immer leise gesprochen.

c) Es wird am Wochenende gespielt.

d) Es wird abends mit Freunden ausgegangen.

e) Es wird nachts in warmen Betten geschlafen.

Ü 14.1)

a) **Machen** Sie bitte das Fenster **zu**!

b) Herr und Frau Müller, **kommen** Sie bitte zur Rezeption!

c) **Sprechen** Sie bitte langsamer!

d) **Schalten** Sie bitte beim Verlassen des Raumes das Licht **aus**!

e) Liebe Gäste, **bringen** Sie bitte ihre eigene Bettwäsche **mit**!

Ü 14.2)

a) Mach bitte das Fenster zu!

b) Herr und Frau Müller, kommt bitte zur Rezeption!

c) Sprich bitte langsamer!

d) Schalte bitte beim Verlassen des Raumes das Licht aus!

e) Liebe Gäste, bringt bitte eure eigene Bettwäsche mit!

Ü 14.3)

a) Karin und Anna, gehen wir einkaufen!

Karin und Anna, lasst uns einkaufen gehen!

b) Dieter, schlafen wir!

Dieter, lass uns schlafen!

c) Herr und Frau Scholz, essen wir!

Herr und Frau Scholz, lasst uns essen!

d) Paul, räumen wir auf!

Paul, lass uns aufräumen!

e) Wolfgang, holen wir Katrin vom Bahnhof ab!

Wolfgang, lass uns Katrin vom Bahnhof abholen!

Ü 15.1)

a) Peter sagte, er stehe morgens nicht gerne auf.

b) Anna und Tom sagten, sie fahren am Sonntag in den Urlaub.

c) Herr Schuster erklärte, er habe bei der Bank einen Kredit aufgenommen.

d) Inge schimpfte, ihr habet euer Zimmer wieder nicht aufgeräumt.

Ü 15.2)

a) Frau Acker berichtete: „Ich habe einen schönen Urlaub gehabt."

b) Olaf sagte: „Ich freue mich auf die große Party."

c) Paul sagte: „Ihr habt Glück mit dem Wetter gehabt."

d) Ich fragte: „Warum ist er noch nicht umgezogen?"

Ü 15.3)

a) Frau Acker berichtete, dass sie einen schönen Urlaub gehabt hat.

Frau Acker berichtete, dass sie einen schönen Urlaub gehabt hätte.

b) Olaf sagte, dass er sich auf die große Party freut.

Olaf sagte, er würde sich auf die große Party freuen.

c) Paul sagte, dass ihr Glück mit dem Wetter gehabt habt.

Paul sagte, ihr habt Glück mit dem Wetter gehabt.

d) Ich fragte, warum er noch nicht umgezogen ist.

Ü 16.1)

	LIEBEN	**KÖNNEN**	**MÖGEN**	**HEISSEN**	**SEHEN**	**WERDEN**
ich	liebte	könnte	möchte	hieße	sähe	würde
du	liebtest	könntest	möchtest	hießest	sähest	würdest
er/sie/es	liebte	könnte	möchte	hieße	sähe	würde
wir	liebten	könnten	möchten	hießen	sähen	würden
ihr	liebtet	könntet	möchtet	hießet	sähet	würdet
sie/Sie	liebten	könnten	möchten	hießen	sähen	würden

Ü 16.2)

a) An deiner Stelle ginge ich nach Hause.

b) An deiner Stelle arbeitete ich mehr.

c) An deiner Stelle brächte ich ihn zum Tierarzt.

d) An deiner Stelle bliebe ich zu Hause.

e) An deiner Stelle würde ich Lehrer.

Ü 16.3)

a) An deiner Stelle würde ich nach Hause gehen.

b) An deiner Stelle würde ich mehr arbeiten.

c) An deiner Stelle würde ich ihn zum Tierarzt bringen.

d) An deiner Stelle würde ich zu Hause bleiben.

e) An deiner Stelle würde ich Lehrer werden.

ALPHABETISCHE VERBLISTE
ALPHABETICAL LIST OF VERBS

Aa

abholen	(to) pick up, (to) collect
abkommen	(to) deviate
abschließen	(to) finish, (to) complete
ankommen	(to) arrive
anrufen	(to) call
ansehen	(to) look at
arbeiten	(to) work
(sich) ärgern	(to) be worked up, (to) get angry
aufgeben	(to) give up
aufheben	(to) save; (to) pick up
aufkommen	(to) arise, (to) emerge
aufräumen	(to) clean/tidy up
aufstehen	(to) get up
aufwachen	(to) wake up
ausgehen	(to) go out

Bb

bauen	(to) build
beantworten	(to) answer (a question)
befehlen	(to) command
bekommen	(to) receive, (to) get
benutzen	(to) use
besitzen	(to) own
bestehen	(to) pass (an exam)
besuchen	(to) visit
bezahlen	(to) pay

brennen	(to) burn
bringen	(to) bring
buchen	(to) book

Dd

denken	(to) think
durchkommen	(to) pull through
dürfen	(to) be allowed to, may

Ee

einkaufen	(to) buy, (to) go shopping
einschlafen	(to) fall asleep
empfangen	(to) receive
empfehlen	(to) recommend
entdecken	(to) discover
entgehen	(to) escape
erkennen	(to) recognize
erklären	(to) explain
erlauben	(to) allow
erleben	(to) experience
erledigen	(to) do, (to) get done
erzählen	(to) tell
essen	(to) eat

Ff

fahren	(to) drive, (to) go
fallen	(to) fall
fangen	(to) catch
fehlen	(to) be missing; (to) lack
feiern	(to) celebrate
finden	(to) find
fliegen (	to) fly

fliehen	(to) flee	leben	(to) live
fließen	(to) flow	lesen	(to) read
folgen	(to) follow	loskommen	(to) get away
freihaben	(to) be free / off		
(sich) freuen	(to) be glad		
funktionieren	(to) work, (to) function		

Gg

geben	(to) give
gebrauchen	(to) utilize
gegenüberstehen	(to) face (each other)
gehen	(to) walk, (to) go
gewinnen	(to) win, (to) gain

Hh

haben	(to) have
halten	(to) hold
heißen	(to) be called
helfen	(to) help
herkommen	(to) come from
horchen	(to) listen (for smth.)
hüpfen	(to) leap

Kk

kaufen	(to) buy
kennen	(to) know, (to) be familiar with
klingeln	(to) ring
kochen	(to) cook; (to) boil
kommen	(to) come
können	(to) be able to, can

Ll

landen	(to) land
lassen	(to) let, (to) leave
laufen	(to) run

Mm

machen	(to) do; (to) make
mähen	(to) mow, (to) cut
missbrauchen	(to) abuse
missverstehen	(to) misunderstand
mitbringen	(to) bring (along)
mitkommen	(to) come along
mögen	(to) like to
müssen	(to) have to, must

Nn

nehmen	(to) take
nennen	(to) name

Oo

öffnen	(to) open

Rr

rauchen	(to) smoke
reisen	(to) travel
reiten	(to) ride
rennen	(to) run, (to) race
rudern	(to) row

Ss

sagen	(to) say
saufen	(to) guzzle; (to) booze
schlagen	(to) beat, (to) hit
schließen	(to) close
schreiben	(to) write
schwimmen	(to) swim
segeln	(to) sail

sehen	(to) see
sein	(to) be
servieren	(to) serve
sinken	(to) sink
sollen	(to) be supposed to, should
spielen	(to) play
sprechen	(to) speak
springen	(to) jump
starten	(to) start, (to) launch
stehen	(to) stand
stehlen	(to) steal
steigen	(to) rise, (to) climb
sterben	(to) die
stoßen	(to) bump; (to) shove
stürzen	(to) fall, (to) tumble

Tt

tanzen	(to) dance
tappen	(to) tiptoe, (to) walk hesitantly
tragen	(to) carry; (to) wear
(sich) treffen	(to) meet (each other)
treffen	(to) meet
trinken	(to) drink

Uu

überlegen	(to) consider, (to) think about
übernehmen	(to) take on, (to) assume
umkommen	(to) perish
umziehen	(to) move, (to) relocate
unterkommen	(to) find accommodation

Vv

(sich) verändern	(to) change

verbrauchen	(to) consume, (to) use up
verdienen	(to) earn
vergessen	(to) forget
verkaufen	(to) sell
verlaufen	(to) proceed, (to) take place
(sich) verletzen	(to) injure oneself
verschlafen	(to) oversleep
verstehen	(to) understand
verwickelt sein	(to) be involved (in smth.)
vorbeikommen	(to) come by, (to) drop by
vorkommen	(to) occur

Ww

wachsen	(to) grow
wandern	(to) hike
warten	(to) wait
waschen	(to) wash
wegkommen	(to) break free
werden	(to) become
werfen	(to) throw
wissen	(to) know
wollen	(to) want to
wünschen	(to) wish

Zz

zerbrechen	(to) break apart
zerstören	(to) destroy
zubereiten	(to) prepare, (to) make
zurückkommen	(to) come back
zusammenkommen	(to) come together

HÄUFIGE UNREGELMÄSSIGE VERBEN
COMMON IRREGULAR VERBS

The following is a list of the most commonly used irregular verbs in German.

- The first column gives the infinitive, which is the form listed in a dictionary.

- The second column lists the English meaning of each verb.

- In the third column you will find the conjugated verb form in the present tense only for those verbs which have an irregularity, namely verbs with a vowel change and verbs where there is a variation in the spelling of the stem or the ending.

- The fourth column lists the simple past form, while column five shows the past participle. Verbs that form the present perfect tense with sein are indicated by an asterisk.

- All verbs with separable prefixes are shown with their prefix split off from the conjugated verb form in columns three and four.

INFINITIVE	MEANING	PRESENT TENSE, VOWEL CHANGE FOR 2ND AND 3RD PERSON SINGULAR	PRÄTERITUM	PAST PARTICIPLE
anfangen	(to) start, begin	fängst an, fängt an	fing an	angefangen
anrufen	(to) call	rufst an, ruft an	rief an	angerufen
aufstehen	(to) get up	stehst auf, steht auf	stand auf	aufgestanden*
beginnen	(to) begin		begann	begonnen
beißen	(to) bite		biss	gebissen
bitten	(to) ask, (to) request	bittest, bittet	bat	gebeten
bleiben	(to) stay		blieb	geblieben*
braten	(to) fry, (to) roast	brätst, brät	briet	gebraten
brennen	(to) burn		brannte	gebrannt
bringen	(to) bring		brachte	gebracht
denken	(to) think		dachte	gedacht
einladen	(to) invite	lädst ein, lädt ein	lud ein	eingeladen
empfehlen	(to) recommend	empfiehlst, empfiehlt	empfahl	empfohlen
essen	(to) eat	isst, isst	aß	gegessen
fahren	(to) go, (to) drive	fährst, fährt	fuhr	gefahren*

fallen	(to) fall	fällst, fällt	fiel	gefallen*
fangen	(to) catch	fängst, fängt	fing	gefangen
finden	(to) find		fand	gefunden
fliegen	(to) fly		flog	geflogen*
geben	(to) give	gibst, gibt	gab	gegeben
gefallen	(to) be pleasing	gefällst, gefällt	gefiel	gefallen
genießen	(to) enjoy	genießt, genießt	genoss	genossen
gewinnen	(to) win		gewann	gewonnen
haben	(to) have	hast, hat	hatte	gehabt
halten	(to) hold; (to) stop	hältst, hält	hielt	gehalten
heißen	(to) be called		hieß	geheißen
helfen	(to) help	hilfst, hilft	half	geholfen
kennen	(to) know		kannte	gekannt
klingen	(to) sound		klang	geklungen
können	(to) be able to	kannst, kann	konnte	gekonnt
lassen	(to) let, (to) allow	lässt, lässt	ließ	gelassen
laufen	(to) run	läufst, läuft	lief	gelaufen*
lesen	(to) read	liest, liest	las	gelesen
lügen	(to) lie		log	gelogen
nehmen	(to) take	nimmst, nimmt	nahm	genommen
raten	(to) advise; (to) guess	rätst, rät	riet	geraten
reiten	(to) ride		ritt	geritten*
riechen	(to) smell		roch	gerochen
rufen	(to) call; (to) shout		rief	gerufen
schlafen	(to) sleep	schläfst, schläft	schlief	geschlafen
schlagen	(to) beat, (to) hit	schlägst, schlägt	schlug	geschlagen
schließen	(to) close	schließt, schließt	schloss	geschlossen
schreiben	(to) write		schrieb	geschrieben
schwimmen	(to) swim		schwamm	geschwommen*
sehen	(to) see	siehst, sieht	sah	gesehen
sein	(to) be	bist, ist	war	gewesen*
senden	(to) send, (to) mail	sendest, sendet	sandte	gesandt
singen	(to) sing		sang	gesungen
sinken	(to) sink		sank	gesunken*
sitzen	(to) sit		saß	gesessen
sprechen	(to) speak	sprichst, spricht	sprach	gesprochen

stehen	(to) stand		stand	gestanden*
sterben	(to) die	stirbst, stirbt	starb	gestorben*
tragen	(to) carry; (to) wear	trägst, trägt	trug	getragen
treffen	(to) meet	triffst, trifft	traf	getroffen
trinken	(to) drink		trank	getrunken
tun	(to) do		tat	getan
umsteigen	(to) change (train etc.)	steigst um, steigt um	stieg um	umgestiegen*
verbinden	(to) connect		verband	verbunden
vergessen	(to) forget	vergisst, vergisst	vergaß	vergessen
verlassen	(to) leave	verlässt, verlässt	verließ	verlassen
verlieren	(to) lose		verlor	verloren
verstehen	(to) understand		verstand	verstanden
verzeihen	(to) forgive		verzieh	verziehen
wachsen	(to) grow	wächst, wächst	wuchs	gewachsen*
waschen	(to) wash	wäschst, wäscht	wusch	gewaschen
werden	(to) become	wirst, wird	wurde	geworden*
werfen	(to) throw	wirfst, wirft	warf	geworfen
wiegen	(to) weigh		wog	gewogen
wissen	(to) know	weißt, weiß	wusste	gewusst
ziehen	(to) pull		zog	gezogen

ALPHABETISCHER ALLGEMEINER WORTSCHATZ
ALPHABETICAL GENERAL VOCABULARY LIST

Aa

(der) Abend [n.]	evening
(das) Abendessen [n.]	dinner
aber [conj.]	but, however
Ach so [interj.]	Oh yes; Oh, I see, …
Ach! [interj.]	Alas!
als [conj.]	when, as
am [prep. Dat.]	at the
(die) Ampel [n.]	traffic light
an [prep.]	at, by
(der) Atem [n.]	breath, breathing
auch [adv.]	also, too
auf [prep.]	on
aus [prep.]	from; out of
(das) Auto [n.]	car
(der) Autounfall [n.]	car accident

Bb

(der) Bahnhof [n.]	(train) station
(der) Balkon [n.]	balcony
(das) Benzin [n.]	gas, petrol, fuel
besonders [adv.]	especially
bestimmt [adv.]	certainly, surely
(der) Besuch [n.]	visitors, guests
(das) Bett [n.]	bed
bevor [conj.]	before
bis [prep.]	until
bis bald [interj.]	see you soon
(der) Bruder [n.]	brother
(das) Buch [n.]	book

Cc

chaotisch [adj.]	chaotic, messy
(der) Chef [n.]	boss, manager
(der) Cognac [n.]	brandy
(der) Computer [n.]	computer

Dd

(der) Dachboden [n.]	attic
Danke [part.]	thank you
dann [adv.]	then; so
(das) Darts [n.]	darts
das [pron.]	that
das hier [pron.]	this here
deine [pron.]	your
den [art. Dat.]	the
deshalb [adv.]	therefore
diese /-r /-es [pron.]	this
doch [part.]	particle for emphasis
du [pron.]	you
dunkel [adj.]	dark, dim
durch [prep.]	through

Ee

ein / -e [adj.]	one
ein [art].	a
eine [art.]	a
einmal [adv.]	once
entspannt [adj.]	relaxed
er [pron.]	he
erste /-r /-s [adj.]	first

(der) Ersti [n.] [coll.]	first-semester student, freshman
es [pron.]	it
(das) Essen [n.]	meal, food
etwas [pron.]	something

Ff

(die) Fahrkarte [n.]	ticket
(die) Familie [n.]	family
(das) Fenster [n.]	window
(der) Film [n.]	movie, film
(die) Fischpfanne [n.]	fish stew
(der) Flug [n.]	flight
(die) Frage [n.]	question
(die) Frau [n.]	woman; wife
(der/die) Freund/-in [n.]	friend
für dich [prep.] [pron.]	for you
(der) Fußball [n.]	soccer, football

Gg

ganz [adj.]	whole, entire
(der) Garten [n.]	backyard, garden
(der) Gast [n.]	guest
gegen [prep.]	against
gemeinsam [adj.]	jointly, together
gerade [adv.]	straight
gern [adv.]	gladly
gern machen [idiom]	(to) love to do
(das) Gesetz [n.]	law
gestern [adv]	yesterday
(die) Gleise [n.]	railroad tracks
grün [adj.]	green
gut [adj.]	good

Hh

halb drei [adv.]	half past two
hallo [interj.]	Hi, Hello
(die) Hand [n.]	hand
häufig [adj.]	frequently
(das) Haus [n.]	house
(die) Hausaufgaben [n. pl.]	homework
(das) Hemd [n.]	shirt
hi [interj.]	hi, hello
hier [adv.]	here
(das) Hobby [n.]	hobby
(die) Hochzeit [n.]	wedding
(der) Hund [n.]	dog

Ii

ich [pron.]	I
ihr [pron.]	you (pl.)
ihr [pron.]	her
ihren [pron. Acc.]	her
im [prep].	in the
immer mehr [adv.]	increasingly (more)
immer noch [adv.]	still
in [prep.]	in
ins [prep. Acc.]	to the

Kk

(der) Kaffee [n.]	coffee
(die) Karten [n. pl.]	cards
(die) Kinder [n. pl.]	children, kids
(das) Kino [n.]	theater, cinema
(das) Klavier [n.]	piano
(das) Klima [n.]	climate
(die) Kneipe [n.]	bar, pub
(das) Konzert [n.]	concert
(der) Kopfhörer [n.]	headphones

(die) Küche [n.]	kitchen	(die) Nachricht [n.]	message
(der) Kuchen [n.]	cake	nächste /-r /-es [adj.]	next
(der) Küchenschrank [n.]	kitchen cabinet	nachts [adv.]	at night
		nahe [adj.]	close, near
Ll		neben [prep.]	next to, beside
		neu [adj.]	new
(der) Laden [n.]	shop, store	nicht [adv.]	not
lange [adv.]	(for) a long time	noch nicht [adv.]	not yet
langsam [adv.]	slowly		
langsamer [adv.]	more slowly	**Oo**	
lecker [adj.]	delicious, yummy		
		oft [adv.]	often
leer [adj.]	empty		
letzte /-r /-s [adj.]	last	**Pp**	
(das) Licht [n.]	light		
		(die) Party [n.]	party
Mm		plötzlich [adv.]	suddenly
		(die) Prüfung [n.]	test, exam
mal [part.]	particle for emphasis		
		Rr	
(der) Mann [n.]	man		
mehr [adv.]	more	(der) Rasen [n.]	lawn, grass
mein [pron].	my	(der) Rasenmäher [n.]	lawnmower
meine [pron.]	my	(der) Rat [n.]	advice
meinen [pron.]	(for) my	ruhig [adj.]	quiet
mich [pron. Acc.]	me		
mit [prep.]	with	**Ss**	
morgen [adv.]	tomorrow		
(der) Motor [n.]	engine	(der) Samstag [n.]	Saturday
müde [adj.]	tired	(der) Schlüsselbund [n.]	key chain
		(die) Schokolade [n]	chocolate
Nn		schön [adj.]	beautiful, nice
		schon [adv.]	already
na [interj.]	So, ... ; Well, ...	(die) Schule [n.]	school
na ja [interj.]	oh well	(die) Schwester [n.]	sister
nach [prep.]	to; after	(die) Schwiegereltern [n.]	parents-in-law
nach Hause [adv.]	home	sein [pron.]	his
nachdem [conj.]	after	seinem [pron. Dat.]	his
nachher [adv.]	afterwards, later	seit [prep.]	since
		seit einiger Zeit [adv.]	for some time

Servus [interj.]	*a greeting, especially common in southern Germany and Austria*	verheiratet [adj.]	married
		(der/die) Vermieter/-in [n.]	landlord
		viel [pron.]	much, a lot
		viele [adj.]	many
		von [prep.]	from, by
sicher [adv.]	surely	vor [prep.]	before, prior
sie [pron.]	she	(die) Vorlesung [n.]	(university) lecture
sie [pron.]	they		
sieben [adj.]	seven		

Ww

so [adv.]	so	wann [adv.]	when
sofort [adv.]	immediately	warum [adv.]	why
(der) Sommer [n.]	summer	was [pron.]	what
(der) Sonntag [n.]	Sunday	(das) Wasser [n.]	water
Spanien [n.]	Spain	weil [conj.]	because
still [adj.]	silent	weiß [adj.]	white
(das) Stück [n.]	(music) piece	wenn [conj.]	when; if
(der) Stuhl [n.]	chair	wie [adv.]	how
		wie geht's?	how are you?

Tt

		wieder [adv.]	again
(der) Taxistand [n.]	taxi stand	wir [pron.]	we
(das) Telefon [n.]	phone	(die) Woche [n.]	week
		(das) Wochenende [n.]	weekend

Uu

		(der) Wochenmarkt [n.]	weekly market
über [prep.]	over, across	woher [adv.]	where from
(die) Uhr [n.]	watch, clock; o'clock	wohl [adv.]	probably
		(die) Wohnung [n.]	apartment, flat
um [prep.]	at (in time indications)		

Zz

und [conj.]	and	zehn [adv.]	ten
unfallfrei [adv.]	without accident	(die) Zeit [n.]	time
		(das) Zimmer [n.]	room

Vv

		zu [adv.]	too
(die) Verantwortung [n.]	responsibility	(der) Zug [n.]	train
verboten [adj.]	forbidden, not allowed	zuhause [adv.]	(at) home
		zur [prep. Dat.]	to the

MORE BOOKS BY LINGO MASTERY

We are not done teaching you German until you're fluent!

Here are some other titles you might find useful in your journey of mastering German:

✓ German Short Stories for Beginners

✓ Intermediate German Short Stories

✓ 2000 Most Common German Words in Context

✓ Conversational German Dialogues

But we got many more!

Check out all of our titles at **www.LingoMastery.com/German**

Printed in Great Britain
by Amazon